Social Casework in General Practice

J. A. S. FORMAN, M.B., B.Chir(Cantab), M.R.C.G.P. and
E.M. FAIRBAIRN, M.A., A.I.M.S.W.

SOCIAL CASEWORK
in General Practice
A report on an experiment carried out
in a General Practice

Published for the Nuffield Provincial Hospitals Trust
by the Oxford University Press 1968
London   New York   Toronto

Oxford University Press, Ely House, London, W1

Glasgow New York Toronto Melbourne Wellington
Cape Town Salisbury Ibadan Nairobi Lusaka Addis Ababa
Bombay Calcutta Madras Karachi Lahore Dacca
Kuala Lumpur Hong Kong Tokyo

Cover design by Edward Bawden
Designed by Bernard Crossland
Drawings by David Anderson

Printed in Great Britain
by Burgess and Son (Abingdon) Ltd., Abingdon, Berks

Contents

References

Acknowledgements

This study was made possible by a generous grant from the Nuffield Provincial Hospitals Trust. We should like to record our thanks for the opportunity of doing the work, and in particular for the open brief given us to develop it.

We are indebted to Professor Wofinden, Bristol University Public Health Department for access to his statistical department. From this department Miss E. H. L. Duncan, Statistician, has guided us in planning, advised us throughout the experiment, and processed our figures for this report; in addition she has given much time to detailed scrutiny of our script. We take this opportunity of recording our warm thanks to her, and to her staff.

Professor Richard Scott and Miss Jane Paterson of the Edinburgh University General Practice Teaching Unit, whose work was a chief inspiration for undertaking this study, gave us valuable advice throughout, in particular in getting the scheme under way.

We were helped by Miss Joan Collins of Cardiff, whose report on medicosocial work in general practice proved a source of valuable information to us.

We also want to thank Dr. R. F. J. H. Pinsent of Birmingham, Research Adviser to the College of General Practitioners; Dr. John Fry of Beckenham; and Miss Hazel Muras, Medical Social Worker, St. Mary's Hospital, London, for their interest and advice in planning.

We have to thank Dr. J. Lyons, M.O.H. Devon County Council, for making possible the inclusion of the Health Visitors in this study, and for his continued interest and enthusiasm.

We have to thank the partners and assistants of the practice, past and present, for their positive participation in the experiment, in the face of unremitting day-to-day pressures of work, and for their numerous contributions to case discussions, and to planning, recording and assessing the work, which have made this in every sense a report from a group practice. We are also indebted to our two attached Health Visitors; to our Receptionists and Secretary; and to other members of our staff, all of whom have been involved to a greater or lesser degree, for their wholehearted co-operation. Several voluntary helpers have added their weight, and to these also we record our thanks.

Lastly our thanks are due to Mrs. M. M. Vowles who has carried the bulk of the secretarial work throughout and whose industry and goodwill have been a major contribution to the production of this report.

PART ONE

Report by J. A. S. Forman

Introduction

'It's another message,' said my daughter, returning from the telephone, and mentioning a well-known name. 'She says "Father's being difficult again". Do you have to go out at this time of night for that?'

Unhappily the message was more specific than it sounded, for from past experience I could interpret it more or less as follows: 'Father, (45, sixteen stone, epileptic psychosis following a head injury) is developing another of his moods of aggression towards his long-suffering wife (40, small, mitral stenosis, past thyroidectomy for thyrotoxicosis) and perhaps towards his children (one on probation), physical violence might be imminent.' So much I know. Beyond this my memory leads me into a partially charted sea of difficult personal relationships within and between the various households of the family; financial anxieties over Father's inability to earn; and social difficulties for the children arising from it all.

Every General Practitioner knows the mixture: defined organic illness, surrounded by less clearly defined social stresses and emotional problems, the last two often demanding as much of his time and energy as the first. And because we have been professionally trained only in the area of organic disease, the socio-emotional side of management may weigh heavily upon us and be disproportionately exhausting and time-consuming.

Of the problems brought to G.P.s for primary assessment, Crombie (4) has estimated that '. . . the emotional component is as important as, or more important than, the organic in 27%; and appreciable in a *further* 21% of diagnostic situations'.

From a rather different angle Professor Antoon Mertens (8) at the Institute of Social Medicine of Nijmegen University has studied the 'social' sources of illness. Three general practitioners attached to the Institute referred cases felt to be in need of social assessment for diagnosis or management to a reviewing board at the Institute. About 400 cases from the three general practices were accepted in the first sixteen months as in need of a social worker's help. This 'minimum estimate' of the need (it was felt unlikely that every case requiring social help had been recognized) is further evidence of the magnitude of the problem before G.P.s.

It is difficult to draw a distinction between social and emotional causes of disability, for they are interdependent. A woman presenting with anxiety symptoms because she is unable to meet the strains of caring for several children in a totally unsuitable house can be looked on as ill for emotional or social reasons. Her own anxiety potential will contribute as well as her housing problem.

Example. A man of about 40 presented with anxiety state sufficient to disable him. He had been employed in a small family business for a long period as a baker. The tempo of work was increasing, and new methods being introduced by younger management, and he found he could not adapt to them. He had always worked with this firm. He had a family of two, and he and his wife had the extra strain of caring for his wife's parents, both invalids. This man was certainly emotionally ill, but his problem can equally well be looked on as a social one. In fact, attention to his social difficulties relieved his anxiety state.

Symptoms presenting in the surgery relate to a wider spectrum of sources than symptoms met in a hospital out-patients' department, where the cases are pre-selected for overt or suspected organic diseases. One way of breaking down the presenting situation in an individual case in general practice is to look separately at the parts played by the *physical* illness, the *personality* of the patient, and the *circumstances* of the patient—'circumstances' being taken, in a wide sense, to mean all the factors of family and social background, including difficult personal relationships between those around him, or between them and himself. We have used this approach in our retrospective assessment of the problems referred to the Medical Social Worker in this experiment.

Example. A man of 61 developed coronary disease and was forced to give up his work as manager of a small laundry business. He had few interests outside his job and being a sociable man, missed the day's work among his long-standing friends; and he found acceptance of the physical restriction imposed on him difficult. A life-long tendency to anxiety and mild depression now came to the fore, and at times he became withdrawn and morose. Finally the financial strictures of ceasing to earn were considerable—he could no longer afford to run a car, and so on. [Management of this problem called for attention to the illness (his coronary disease and its physical effects), the personality (his anxiety-depressive nature with limited interests or adaptability), and the circumstances (his loss of companionship and financial problems; and the possibility of finding acceptable sedentary work for him).]

Without labouring the value of this obvious but practical break-down of illness situations, it can be said that it helps to clarify the various needs of patients; and in this report to indicate the relative proportions of these three facets of general practice medicine. Not every case has roots in all three categories, but it is helpful to keep them in mind in making assessment of new situations, or in considering management.

In our series of medicosocial cases, as might be expected, nearly all cases had significant circumstantial elements, and the category 'circumstances' was broken down into numerous sub-categories to indicate social needs as shown in Fig. 8 (p. 28).

The Management of medicosocial work in general practice

It is impossible to practise domiciliary medicine without involvement in social and emotional problems. But it is unrealistic to think that sufficient time can be found by G.P.s to make the necessary full analysis of these factors for a patient population of between two and three thousand, in addition to meeting the rapidly increasing demands of strictly 'clinical' medicine. This remains true even if, as G.P.s, we were adequately trained in this area of medical care, which at present we are not.

There is thus an important gap in domiciliary medical care, neglect of which leads to a continuing quantum of illness and unhappiness, which can be reduced only if better provision is made for its management. Patients needing help with social or emotional problems are often patients who make heavy demands on their doctors, the more so because in this work G.P.s have insufficient basic training, and are therefore less at home with and less successful than when dealing with physical illness.

Not all of these patients can be helped, but many can. It is likely that much of this kind of disability is preventable if identified early.

For we are not looking at a group of neurotic patients with self-limiting complaints; but at 'normal' people reacting to difficult situations, most of which can be ameliorated, nearly all of which can be made tolerable, with relief of symptoms, and return to independence of the sufferer. 'Sufferer' is used here advisedly, because medical care cannot afford to neglect states of happiness and unhappiness; misery, fear, and depression are not compatible with positive health. They predispose to, and breed ill-health.

But, whether analysis of the social and emotional forces at work are useful in altering the patient's situation beneficially or not, it invariably puts the G.P. in a stronger position to deal with the patient or his family's future illnesses and crises, and it gives information and insight where these may have been lacking. When the range and bounds of a problem are defined, it becomes less difficult to meet.

A practical attempt to better this area of medical care by the attachment of a M.S.W. (Almoner)[1] to a group practice to work with its G.P.s on day-to-day problems is the subject of this experiment. The M.S.W. was fully identified with the practice; she worked from its premises, restricted herself to its patients, and had no outside appointments or obligations.

---

1. When we began this experiment the familiar name 'Almoner' was still in use. It has since been altered to 'Medical Social Worker', with which it is synonymous. For brevity, the initials M.S.W. are used in this account.

1. The experiment

The objects of the experiment

The primary object of the experiment was very simple:

To estimate the value, if any, of a M.S.W. in a group practice, by a three-year trial attachment.

Three further objects were then defined:

To make some analysis of the problems referred to her.

To estimate the need for medicosocial work in the practice.

To estimate the value of a general practice as a site for a M.S.W., in making contact with those in need of her service.

During the second and third year of the experiment two Health Visitors were attached to the practice by courtesy of the Medical Officer of Health, and it has been possible to make some study, as a subsidiary objective, of our experience of the relative roles of the M.S.W. and H.V. This experience is discussed in Chapter 8.

Previous work

Although general practice is so intimately bound up with social and emotional stresses, attempts at real integration between G.P.s and M.S.W.s have been few. Professor Richard Scott and Miss Jane Paterson M.S.W. at the Edinburgh University General Practice Teaching Unit have some twenty years' experience of working together and of teaching in general practice. This was the chief stimulus for the present experiment (**12, 10**).

Backett, Maybin, and Yvonne Dudgeon investigated the social work content of a Northern Irish practice over one year in 1954–5 (**1**) and concluded that a specially trained social worker might cover the work of a practice of 4,000 patients.

Further information came from Madge Dongray (5, 6) working at Darbishire House, the Manchester University Health Centre, in 1955–8; and from Joan Collins (3), working from Cardiff University, with attachment to a Cardiff group practice, for one year, with a year's follow-up study, in 1961–2. All these have filled a hitherto unmet need for their services in general practice.

Other writers who have helped our understanding in this experiment have been Querido (11) in Holland, who demonstrated the importance and practicability of assessing socio-emotional factors in prognosis for recovery of surgical patients; Harrington (7) on *Psychotherapy in General Practice*; and Michael Balint (2).

A study of medicosocial work in general practice is currently being carried out at Nijmegen University in Holland by the Institute of Social Medicine under Professor Mertens, in co-operation with three general practitioners (8), and we have been privileged to see how this has been approached and carried out.

The importance of the social work facet of general practice was discussed in the Gillie Report *The Field of Work of the General Practitioner* (15); and in the College of General Practitioners' publication *Special Vocational Training for General Practice* (14).

The setting of the experiment

The work was carried out in a group practice of six partners based on a practice-owned central surgery. For many years it has been our policy to employ a bigger than average ancillary team, to enable us to delegate non-clinical duties (a custom commoner in the south-west of England than in some other areas). The work-load is heavy, and we rely on our staff to carry receptionist, clerical, nursing and dispensing work, correspondence, and the handling of records. The M.S.W. has had at her disposal the facilities we use ourselves. Without the willing support of our staff the experiment could not have been carried through, and it is unlikely that without this sort of organization we, as G.P.s, would have reached a point in our concept of medical care at which realization of our needs in medicosocial care became 'the next problem to tackle'.

Out staff comprises a nurse; a full-time typist; the equivalent of three and a half full-time receptionists (most are part-time); two full-time dispensers, aided by some part-time help; a part-time book-keeper; and a resident caretaker and his wife who handle cleaning and maintenance. During this experiment we have had additional part-time secretarial help for the M.S.W. We have also benefited greatly from part-time voluntary work from a number of helpers.

For the past two years the two H.V.s previously mentioned have augmented this surgery community.

The practice is sited in a country town of 20,000 population, and its 14,400 patients are almost equally divided between town and country, the radius of travel being 8—12 miles in the various direc-tions. The town has about a dozen factories, and the rural population is predominantly agricultural. The practice population reflects the population locally in respect of class, age-structure, and occupation. The area is somewhat isolated geographically, and is nearly 100 miles from the nearest university medical faculty.

Several changes in partnership occurred in the three years of the experiment (1963–6) and this, with the passage of a Trainee Assistant through it, led to nine G.P.s in all being associated with the work. Four partners saw the work through from start to finish.

The practice has always had a personal approach to medical care. The majority of patients remain attached to one partner (covered by others when off duty) and this is consciously encouraged by all. Many families have been attended by members of the practice for two, three, or four generations, and there are widespread family-to-practice loyalties. Habitually the bounds of medical care are set beyond the limits of purely clinical responsibility, and include involvement in personal, family, and social problems.

2. The content of the Medical Social Worker's contribution

The sort of help the M.S.W. has given the practice in this experiment covers a wide canvas, but may be divided into two categories:

1. A case-work service for complex social and emotional situation surrounding illnesses, or presenting in the surgery in the guise of physical illness.

2. Effective mobilization of the Social Services.

Casework

It is not possible to work for long with a M.S.W. without coming to grips with this important but elusive word. Readers familiar with it will perhaps bear with an attempt to define its meaning for those G.P.s who, like ourselves three years ago, may be hazy about its meaning.

It has been defined as: 'A personal service, provided by qualified workers, for individuals who require skilled assistance in resolving some material, emotional or character problem. . . .' The full definition, here quoted in short, may be found in the *Report of the Working Party on Social Workers in the Local Health and Welfare Services* (Younghusband Report) (13).

Casework in the context of medical practice may be looked on as the assessment of a patient's or family's total situation, taking account of environmental forces, personality, and physical illness; bringing the patient along with this assessment, if he is able, and at his own pace, so that he defines his problem; giving such assistance as is necessary for him to find solutions; and/or providing support in situations which cannot be altered.

This is familiar ground to G.P.s; we are called upon to do it continually. By experience, rule of thumb, and such intuition as we can muster, we make a better or a worse job of it according to our ability. A great deal depends on our knowledge of individual families, and on the time we have available. But we have no specific training for it, and our clinical education tends to lead us away from it, and towards the more concrete matters of physical signs and laboratory reports. Exclusive attention to these may lead us to turn out backs on half of the patient's problem, and so fail in both diagnosis and management.

In this experiment it has been the casework skill of the M.S.W. which has been her major contribution. In cases we have referred to her we have had the great benefit of full information about the patient or family so allowing complete diagnosis for planning a rational course of management. The therapeutic value of the process of listening, discussion, and support has been very clear, and sometimes this was all that was required for a patient to solve his own problem. Beyond 'lengthening our arm' in this way the M.S.W. has brought new insights into our work; and in management she has completed medical care by dealing effectively with the social and emotional side of problems.

The type of social and emotional problems referred to the M.S.W. in this experiment needs some definition. Patients suffering from major psychoses were not referred, as it was felt that these were already well provided for by the psychiatric services and by ourselves. Likewise problem families were not referred, as being already in receipt of a great deal of attention from the H.V.s, the Welfare Department, and ourselves. (For various reasons a few cases in either category found their way into her series).

In principle we aimed to refer patients who were normally independent and able to deal with their problems, but who were for the time being disabled, or threatened with disablement, by events in their lives—for example, a major long-term illness, bereavement, threatened family breakdown—where early assistance had some prospect of restoring the balance or giving effective support over a crisis. This is to say that the M.S.W. was chiefly dealing with normal (or paranormal) reactions to disease and/or social and emotional stresses.

The analysis of the 'Nature of the problems' referred to here is dealt with in Chapter 4.

Stress and the General Practitioner

It is commonly argued that the effects of stress, whether from physical disease, social pressures, or difficulties of personality or personal relationship, need not be seen as a part of medical care, and could be dealt with by a casework service working aside from the medical services. In this practice we recognize our lack of time to cover this work, and our lack of training for it; but these problems nevertheless continually present to us, and perforce occupy a large part of our time and attention. They may force themselves on us as the emotional reaction to physical illness, or present, paradoxically, as social or emotional problems in the guise of physical illness, i.e. with physical symptons. It is often far from easy, in searching for the source of presenting symptoms, to differentiate between physical and emotional causes, and indeed this is one of the most demanding problems before the G.P. in screening large numbers of patients quickly. For obvious reasons this differential diagnosis requires medical skills, and to this extent at least G.P.s are, and must be, involved in social and emotional stress reactions.

In managing a physical illness at home the social and emotional components can seldom be separated from the physical; management essentially takes both into account. The amount of serious social and emotional stress met in everday general practice is very great, and while more time and skill are badly needed, it does not seem likely that much of this work can be dissociated from *medical* care. Rather medical care needs to embody the support of medico-social skills.

Effective mobilization of the Social Services

The term 'Social Services' is here used in a very wide sense, to include besides the statutory and voluntary Social Services, housing authorities, schools, the police, personnel managers, employers, neighbours, well-disposed persons of no other denomination, and so on. The full list of 'Agencies contacted' will be found in Part Two, 2, Fig. 26, which illustrates the size of the problem. These all fall into a group as seen from the surgery, for all can, and indeed must be drawn on for help. Their effective mobilization depends on three factors: knowledge of their existence, time to communicate with them, and, far from least, the skill to enlist their active and continuing interest, so that the service called upon makes an effective contribution as opposed to going through the motions of doing it. This last skill includes drive in getting problems through to the appropriate individual (not organization), the ability to stimulate interest and action, and the persistence to see that the work has in fact been done in follow-up.

Example. An elderly woman who had spent many years in a mental hospital with chronic schizophrenia, but had lived in the community for about ten years latterly, had repeated difficulty with lodgings, moving from one to another, and constantly coming to the surgery for help. It was plain that at times she was not adequately cared for; this may or may not have been related to intermittent relapse of schizophrenic symptoms, which commonly caused another change of lodgings. She was a lonely, inadequate but not unlikeable individual, with no family support and no close friends. On more than one occasion her G.P. felt she was unfit for life in the community, but referral for re-admission to a psychiatric hospital was (possibly rightly) turned down. The psychiatric history weighed against her in application to either of the old people's homes locally. The Welfare Office, and Mental Welfare Officers took a part, but found no permanent solution, and the patient continued to drift from lodging to lodging, and to frequent the surgery for moral support.

The M.S.W., after assessing the patient and trying various avenues, successfully placed her with a small private home where four or five elderly people were cared for. Success depended very much on winning mutual acceptance from the patient and the owner of the home, the kind of operation which calls for time, patience, and indeed, casework skill. The M.S.W.'s function here in finding and mobilizing an appropriate social service (in this instance not a statutory one) was reflected many times in the series. (See Fig. 26, p. 102: *Link with Social Services*).

On the subject of constantly seeing the G.P. it was acknowledged that she 'had to talk to someone'. The patient commented: 'Yes, and I haven't any relatives. The Welfare people are supposed to look after me.' This is not quoted as a reflection on the Welfare Department, but to instance the need in general practice for a social worker who sees the problem from the G.P.'s side, and who will personally see the patient through socially, as the G.P. sees her through medically.

3. Method of working wtih the Medical Social Worker

It was decided at the outset that patients should reach the M.S.W. by referral from the G.P.s, and that the G.P.s would refer such patients as they felt she could help, or for whom they lacked information on social background, or when stresses of unknown origin were suspected. It was appreciated that it would take time for the G.P.s to know the M.S.W.'s capabilities and limitations, and that selection of cases for referral would improve with experience.

An alternative policy, that the M.S.W. should screen sections of the practice, or screen such patient groups as hospital-leavers, cancer patients, or pre-operative patients, was turned down for the following reasons:

1. It was foreseen that demand would outstrip supply of M.S.W. time, and that the best use of her time would be made by referring cases of known or believed need.

2. Joan Collins (3) in Cardiff had found that much time was wasted in screening 'categories' of patients to find patients in serious need amongst them. By no means all hospital-leavers, for instance, need a M.S.W.s help.

3. Patients who come to the doctor for help with a problem are *at that time* in need and therefore willing to consult a M.S.W., and likely to be accessible to her. The same is not true of patients selected by 'category', and we felt those not in need of help might resent the interference.

These decisions were found sound in practice. In a group of G.P.s there is much more medicosocial work than one M.S.W. can undertake. We were, and are, satisfied that the way to achieve the best selection of patients is by the G.P. becoming familiar with the

M.S.W.'s work and capabilities, and training himself to select those in greatest need as they arise in the course of the week's work. In this, the M.S.W. and G.P.s have a mutual educational role.

By the end of the series, however, 41 patients out of the total of 409 had been referred to the M.S.W., not by the G.P. but through requests from patients, relatives, social workers, and others. In these cases the M.S.W. accepted the referral after consultation with the G.P. concerned. In general, before referring a patient to the M.S.W. we felt it important to put the proposition to him, explaining that the M.S.W. might be able to help; and pointing out that contact could always be broken if found unhelpful. It was sometimes necessary to give the patient a day or two to think this over. Very few refused. The patient and M.S.W. were then introduced, after briefing the M.S.W. with an outline of the situation as seen at the time by the G.P.

In making initial contact we found it often an advantage to be able to assure the patient that the M.S.W. was not only a professional person with respect for clinical and social confidences, but also a member of the practice, working with us, and from the practice premises. Some patients would undoubtedly have accepted referral to the M.S.W. wherever she had been working; but people have reservations about disclosing their personal affairs to anyone beyond their doctor, when it is he they have come to consult, and we think that many would have declined referral 'outside the practice'. We have no measure of this.

The Patient–General Practitioner–Medical Social Worker triangle

Once referred, it was understood by patient, M.S.W., and G.P. that confidences would be exchanged within this triangle, and that the problem called for active co-operation by each member of it. This amounted to enlargement of the doctor–patient relationship to a doctor–patient–M.S.W. relationship, and we had some initial misgivings about the possibility or wisdom of this. These were unfounded. The great majority of patients appreciated the added help, and many expressed their gratitude to the M.S.W. and to the G.P.s for taking the trouble to bring her into the problem. The doctor–patient relationship suffered nothing. It was usually strengthened by virtue of the G.P.s increased knowledge of the situation and better understanding of it. The threat to the doctor–patient relationship is a myth—provided always that there is mutual confidence and a high standard of communication and understanding between G.P. and M.S.W.

Communication between G.P. and M.S.W. on the progress of cases was mainly by intermittent discussion on patients currently being seen by one or other or both. Most of us arranged a regular weekly session for this of half to one hour; in addition there were numerous *ad hoc* exchanges, and a little use of notes and telephone messages. Usually patients saw the G.P. and M.S.W. separately, but occasionally triangular consultations were useful.

Learning to work together

The G.P.'s initial problem was to grasp the nature of the M.S.W.'s role and appreciate her capabilities and limitations. The art of identifying the most suitable problems to refer to the M.S.W. came reasonably quickly; but like other medical arts this continues to improve with practice. As the experiment proceeded there was perhaps some shift away from asking the M.S.W. to perform some specific function in a case, towards bringing her into a problem for her specialist knowledge and skills, and expecting her to proceed in any way she found indicated. This does not remove ultimate responsibility from the G.P. in charge for what is done and it therefore demands frequent communication and continued sharing of informations on progress.

The M.S.W. was faced with a formidable task at the outset. In addition to exploring the statutory, voluntary, and other social services of an unknown area, she had to assimilate for the first time the content and methods of general practice. She met, as all G.P.s have met, the frustrations of grossly inadequate time for the job to be done; of work-demands exceeding time and strength; of the emotional stresses of involvements in patients' personal tragedies, and how at home these can weigh more heavily and with greater continuity than they may in hospital work. She had to adapt her interview technique and recording to faster speeds and greater conciseness, as G.P.s have had to do in consultation and note-making, without moving too fast for her patients, or becoming too shallow in her assessments.

In addition she was working in an area boasting only one hospital M.S.W. (*none* in the second half of the experiment) and so worked without consultation or discussion with her own kind.

There was certainly some imbalance in the confrontation of six (sometimes more) G.P.s with one M.S.W., and it was interesting to find that this had been better appreciated in the experimental work we saw at Nijmegen, where three social workers balanced three G.P.s on the case-selection committee (8).

Seminars

Experience at the Edinburgh University General Practice Unit (Professor R. Scott and Jane Paterson) led us to hold a series of seminars, in which the M.S.W. and the G.P. concerned presented a difficult or unsolved medicosocial problem to the remainder of the partnership. On occasion visitors were invited, such as the Consultant in Child Guidance, a family caseworker from the Welfare Office, or a G.P. from outside the practice. These meetings were held in the surgery over bread and cheese lunches. They formed a valuable vehicle for exchange of ideas, facts, and attitudes between partners, and gave a new dimension to inter-partner communication. They illustrated how different partners were using the M.S.W., and helped to establish her most useful roles. They contributed ideas and suggested actions on the cases discussed. And by bringing us to extract ourselves from the daily pressures of practice to discuss a common problem, they reduced the personal frictions and irritations which arise in conditions of overwork.

4. Assessment of the work done

Measuring the effect of a M.S.W.'s work presents formidable problems. The situations referred to her in this experiment were generally complex problems involving social circumstance, personality, and physical illness; in a series of about 400 cases it is not to be expected that parallel situations, in any sense comparable to them, can be found for use as controls. In addition, the effects of the work done in some cases may not be visible, far less measurable, for months or years to come.

In planning we felt the nearest we could get to an objective assessment of each case was to ask the G.P. in charge, at the point of closure of the case, to complete a questionnaire, with a point-rating system. Thus his knowledge of the total situation was used to evaluate the M.S.W.'s contribution in relation to its diagnosis and management. This at least would record each G.P.'s opinion on its value. We also decided to ask each G.P. to give an opinion on three other points: the degree to which the M.S.W. was covering new ground in her work (i.e. working in an area of unmet need as opposed to the degree to which she was relieving the G.P., or others, of work which would have been done or attempted in her absence); whether or not a H.V. could have carried out the work done; and in what way the M.S.W.'s work contributed, whether in diagnosis, therapy, as a link with the social services, or in prophylaxis.

We also wanted to analyse the sources of medicosocial illness which brought patients to us. The M.S.W., at the point of closure of each case, was asked to make a detailed assessment of the sources of the problem. She was also asked to record in categorized form the actions taken on the case.

The M.S.W. also made a summary of each case in retrospect, and to this the G.P.s added comments. This proved a useful way of crystallising our final thoughts on each case.

Finally, the M.S.W. kept a full record of personal and social details of her cases; she recorded the time spent on each, and the time-span of contact; the number of consultations held with the G.P., and with other colleagues; and the social agencies contacted in the course of the work.

The pitfalls of using value-judgements to assess the work done were appreciated. But it was thought that retrospective assessment of each case by the G.P. concerned and by the M.S.W. would give some degree of objectivity, more especially as several G.P.s (in the event, nine) would be contributing.

After committing ourselves to a great deal of work in making this assessment of each patient and planning to process the results, it was a comfort to find, on visiting Holland nearly three years later, that a very similar method of assessment, using point-ratings, had been adopted at the Institute of Social Medicine at Nijmegen University.

Assessment of patient-opinion was considered but rejected for two reasons. It was thought that assessment of their comments would demand considerable insight into, and perhaps knowledge of, the patients and their families, and it would be difficult to find anyone suitably qualified (for example, a retired partner) who would not be open to criticism on grounds of bias. Secondly, the informed opinions we sounded were lukewarm about the value of any attempt to assess patient-opinion in this sort of work.

Our method of assessment is described in greater detail in the following pages, and with it are shown the aggregated figures for our 409 cases. There are two parts:

Part 1. Retrospective assessment by the G.P. referring the case.

Part 2. Retrospective assessment by the M.S.W. of the *nature of the problem* referred and the *actions taken* by her.

Neither of these sections record facts. They record individual value-judgements and opinions made in retrospect on the work done.[1]

1. Analysis of factual information from the M.S.W.'s records will be found in Part Two, 2, p. 64.

I. Retrospective assessment by the General Practitioner

At or after the closure of each case the G.P. in charge completed a standard questionnaire, which is reproduced below.

Fig. 1. *The General Practitioner questionnaire*

1. Estimate the M.S.W.'s contribution to your handling of this case/ incident relative to other measures in the diagnosis and management.

The major factor	Much help	Some help	No help	Harmful	Help refused

2. (*a*) If the M.S.W.'s contribution was helpful, would the work have been covered in her absence?

Yes	No

(*b*) If *Yes*, by:

Yourself	Surgery staff	Existing Social Services	Others

(*c*) As adequately?

Yes	No

3. Could the H.V. attached to you have dealt with this problem

As effectively	Partially	No

4. Classify the M.S.W.'s contribution (tick every box).

Diagnostic		Therapeutic		Link with Social Services		Prophylactic	
Yes	No	Yes	No	Yes	No	Yes	No

Question 1. (*Estimate the M.S.W.'s contribution to your handling of this case/incident, relative to other measures in the diagnosis and management.*)

This was designed to measure the place of the M.S.W.'s contribution, if any, in dealing with the problem presented. It is important to note that the G.P.s were *not* asked simply to rate the value of the M.S.W.'s work. They were asked to indicate its place in dealing with a problem *vis-a-vis* other measures, such as drugs, consultant opinion or therapy, or G.P.'s management. It is an attempt to measure the medicosocial element in the diagnosis and management of a total situation.

The 409 cases referred to the M.S.W. were assessed as follows using the six-point rating:

Fig. 2. *Aggregated figures from nine General Practitioners' recordings*

	The major factor	Much help	Some help	No help	Harmful	Help refused	Not assessed
Cases	62	155	167	23	nil	1	1
Percentage	15·2	37·9	40·8	5·6	nil	0·2	0·2

This indicates that in the several opinions of the G.P.s taking part, the M.S.W.'s contribution was helpful in some degree in 93·9 per cent of the cases referred; and was rated as 'much help' or 'the major factor' in 53·1 per cent.

Question 2 a, b, and **c** was designed to indicate to what extent the M.S.W. was providing a service which was covering new ground, i.e. filling an unmet need; and to what extent she was relieving the G.P.s and others of work which they themselves would have carried out, or attempted to carry out, in her absence. The questions were answered as follows:

a. *If the M.S.W.'s contribution was helpful, would her work have been covered in her absence?*
The M.S.W.'s contribution was recorded as helpful in some degree in 384 cases (93·9 per cent). Fig. 3 shows how this question was answered.

Fig. 3. *Would the Medical Social Worker's work have been covered in her absence?*

	Yes	No	No helpful contribution	Not assessed	Total
Cases	216	168	24	1	409
Percentage of series of 409 cases	52·9	41·1	5·9	0·2	100

This shows that in the opinion of the recording G.P.s the work done by the M.S.W. on 41·1 per cent of the total cases would *not* have been covered in her absence. For those working in the experiment there is no question of this work having been unnecessary, trivial, or a luxury addition to medical care. It was work basic to complete diagnosis or management in the cases referred. The figure of 41·1 per cent of the total cases is therefore read as a measure of *the unmet need* for this service in the practice.

b. *If Yes, by whom?*

Question 2*a* above was answered *yes* in 216 cases, indicating that in these the M.S.W.'s work *would* have been covered in her absence (though not necessarily as adequately). Question 2*b* was designed to demonstrate to whom the work would have fallen in the absence of the M.S.W. The way it was answered is shown in Fig. 4.

Fig. 4. *Who would have covered the Medical Social Worker's work in her absence?*

	Yourself (G.P.)	Surgery staff	Existing Social Services	Other	Total
Number of entries[1]	140	19	123	6	288[1]
Percentage of total series of 409	34·2	4·6	30·0	1·4	

1. In some cases the recording G.P. felt that the problem could have been handled by more than one of the above, for example, by himself, or by existing Social Services, and two columns were marked. Hence the total of 288 entries exceeds the total of 216 cases under consideration.

It can be seen that in 140 cases (34·2 per cent of the total series) it was estimated that the G.P. himself would have handled or attempted to handle the problem. This can be taken as a rough measure of the *G.P.–time saved* by the M.S.W. (It should be noted, however, that this takes no account of the future time saved for the G.P. when a medicosocial problem is fully analysed and disposed of. This is further discussed in Chapter 5.) *Existing Social Services* it was thought, could have dealt with 123 cases (30 per cent of the total series) though not necessarily as adequately. It may be asked why they were not brought into play in place of the M.S.W.   This is discussed in Chapter 7 and in Part Two, 1.

c. *As adequately?*

Question 2*a* was answered *yes* in 216 cases and the answers given to Question 2*b* indicate by whom the work would have been covered in the M.S.W.'s absence. Question 2*c* asked whether, in the opinion of the recording G.P. the work would have been done as adequately in these circumstances. Fig. 5 shows how this question was answered.

This indicates that in exactly half the cases (108) it was thought that existing services would have dealt with the problems *less adequately* than the M.S.W. This is taken to indicate *further unmet need* for the M.S.W.'s service. One hundred and eight cases represent 26·4 per cent of the total series of 409.

Question 3. *Could the H.V. attached to you have dealt with this problem?*

It was felt that the relative roles of the M.S.W. and the H.V.s were a specific point of interest and that it should be considered in isolation. The question was applicable only to the cases referred in the second half of the experiment, as two H.V.s were attached to the

Fig. 5. *Would coverage have been as adequate in the Medical Social Worker's absence?*

	Yes	*No*	*Total*
Number of cases	108	108	216

practice in November 1964, one year after the project started, and were worked in and known to us sufficiently to allow this rating over the last eighteen months of the experiment. Each H.V. was attached to the practice of certain of the partners, and worked closely with them. In this context we felt able to complete this rating *in respect of the H.V. attached to each of us* (but not to H.V.s as a genus). This is more fully discussed in Chapter 8.

We had some doubts about our qualifications to make these judgements, but felt that in the unusual situation of having both a M.S.W. and H.V.s attached to the practice, the opinions of the G.P.s working with them would be worth recording. The question was answered as follows (Fig. 6):

Fig. 6. *Could the Health Visitor attached to you have dealt with the problem?*

	As effectively	Partially	No	Total
Cases	75	97	101	273
Percentage of this series of 273 cases	27·5	35·6	37·0	100

The 273 cases in this series were part of the total series of cases selected by the G.P.s for referral to the M.S.W. and it is therefore not surprising that in only 27·5 per cent. of them was it considered that the H.V. could have dealt with them as effectively. It may be asked why in fact this 27·5 per cent. were not referred to a H.V. and not the M.S.W.; but it should be remembered that this three-point rating was made in retrospect. At the point of first contact with a problem its content and complexity has yet to be assessed.

This series clearly shows that in the opinion of the G.P.s recording there is a field of work in which the M.S.W.'s contribution was outside the range of the H.V.s—absolutely in 37 per cent., and partially in 35·6 per cent. of the series, together 72·6 per cent. There seem to us very obvious reasons why this should be so, as our H.V.s have no specific training in medicosocial casework. This is more fully discussed in Chapter 8 to which the reader is referred. It may be stated in this context however that our two H.V.s are of very high calibre, and our claims on their help have been very heavy. Their addition to the practice has greatly added to the value of our total effort in medical care, but largely in a different field of work from the M.S.W.s.

Item 4 of the questionnaire, 'Classify the M.S.W.'s contribution', was designed to show a pattern of the sort of help the M.S.W. was giving the G.P.s, whether diagnostic, therapeutic, or as a link with the Social Services; and whether in their eyes it had prophylactic value. From the recorded opinions, these figures emerge (Fig. 7):

Fig. 7.[1] *Classification of the Medical Social Worker's contribution*

	Diagnostic	Therapeutic	Link with Social Services	Prophylactic	No M.S.W. contribution	No assessment
Number of cases	42	243	255	140	23	2
Percentage of total series of 409 cases	10·3	59·4	62·3	34·2	5·6	0·5

This pattern shows that the recording G.P.s estimated that help in *Therapy* and help as a *Link with Social Services* were predominant, each being marked in about 60 per cent. of the total series of cases. It is of interest that in 34 per cent., *Prophylactic value* was seen in the work done. The figure for *Diagnostic value* of 10·3 per cent. indicates those cases where the M.S.W.'s work made, changed, or confirmed the diagnosis. Although not recorded it can be safely stated that the G.P.'s diagnosis was enlarged, or made in greater detail, in many more cases than these. For further illustration of the M.S.W.'s function as a link with the Social Services see also Part Two, 2, Part Two, 6, and Fig. 26, p. 102.

II. Retrospective assessment by the Medical Social Worker

1. *The nature of the problems referred*

Most problems sufficient to cause social or emotional illness are conditioned by more than one factor, and it is usually not possible,

---

1. As cases were frequently entered in more than one column the total entries exceed the total number of cases, and the total percentages exceed 100.

if the analysis is to be more than superficial, to put them into simple categories, such as, for instance, 'housing problem', 'reaction to physical illness', or 'difficulty with personal relationships'.

Example. A woman crippled by congenital lower-limb deformities, moved with her farm worker husband on retirement to a town basement flat. Above her lived her daughter, son-in-law, and their child of four. This marriage was going badly, and there was open discord and often violence, frightening to the four-year-old. The grandmother's anxieties over the child were acute and well-founded. But she was unable to 'interfere' beneficially, or find a solution. Her locomotor defect imprisoned her with the situation all day, for she could not manage the steep and dangerous basement steps unaided. When she called her G.P. he found her physically and emotionally exhausted and dangerously depressed.

To this problem her physical disability, the unsuitability of the house, the disordered personal relationships above, and perhaps her natural limitations in resource, had all contributed. All these required assessment before an effective plan of management could be attempted.

Example. A young man working as a sales storeman presented with anxiety symptoms and epigastric pain. He was known to have had a duodenal ulcer. He had a tendency to over-react to anxieties, and inquiry revealed a real one as regards housing. He and his wife and child of three had put up with life In an upstairs single room, with shared lavatory and no play space since the child was born; his wife had now started her second pregnancy, and had no doubt put pressure on her husband to find something better. They were still a long way from the top of the waiting-list for a council house, and had not the means to buy. A letter from the G.P. to the Housing Authority had not helped. The husband reacted by going sick with anxiety symptoms and there seemed a clear relationship with the relapse of his duodenal ulcer. The factors which brought him to the doctor included the housing situation, his own anxiety potential, and his duodenal ulcer, the situation being brought to a head by his wife's second pregnancy.

It was thought useful, therefore, to record the various elements estimated to have contributed to each patient's problem, recording one, two, three, or if necessary more ingredients. By recording in this way we have been able to build up a spectrum of causative elements for the whole series of cases, which indicates what was common and what was rare.

Three major categories, already referred to in the Introduction, were used in assessing the causative elements of the problems referred to the M.S.W. They were the illness, the personality, and the circumstances of the patient.

Illness was defined as organic disease, in which was included for the purposes of this experiment the major psychoses (for example, schizophrenia, depression sufficient to warrant a psychiatrist's opinion or care), but not including psychosomatic symptoms. This category—illness—was not further subdivided.

Personality. For 'personality' to be rated as a causative factor in a problem there had to be evidence of personality difficulties or aberration preceding the present situation, and assessed from the history and behaviour of the patient to have contributed to (not arisen from) the current situation. This included patients whose limited intelligence was a contributory factor. This category—personality—was not further subdivided.

Circumstances. These were the social and environmental factors presenting a current stress and contributing to the patient's problem, and they form a major part of our list. This category was subdivided into such factors as 'Housing', 'Finance', 'Widowhood', as shown below. For practical reasons this section also included a group of difficult personal relationships (for example, parent–child relationships) either in the patient's own relationships, or between others in his environment, which materially affected the problem.

We purposely avoided a preconceived list of these sub-categories, and our headings were built up out of our experience as we progressed, categories being added as found necessary. Categorization therefore, grew out of working experience.

The categories are in effect various sources of social or emotional stress which were estimated by the M.S.W. to contribute to the patient's need for help, in making a retrospective review of the case.

Breaking down a total situation into these categories and sub-categories proved a practical way of clarifying the problem and of identifying the sources of difficulty.

The list of categories we found necessary in analysing the nature of the problems referred to the M.S.W. is shown in Fig. 8, with the total number of cases which were entered in each. Comparison of these numbers indicates the frequency with which identified sources of stress were met in the series.

Fig. 8

	Cases	Percentage of total series of 409	
ILLNESS	231	56·5	
PERSONALITY	205	50·1	
CIRCUMSTANCES Total	405	99·0	
Schooling	10	2·4	
Occupation	95	23·2	*Practical*
Housing	109	6·7	*social*
Finance	63	15·4	*problems*
Miscellaneous	93	22·7	
Fatigue and/or worry	25	6·1	Total 338 cases
Registered problem family	6	1·5	
Poor home management	17	4·2	82·6 per cent.
Geriatric difficulties	99	24·2	
Adolescent difficulties	15	3·7	*Personal*
Marital difficulties	46	11·2	*relationship*
Parent–child difficulties	31	7·6	*difficulties*
Relatives difficulties	25	6·1	
Solitary living	13	3·2	Total 148 cases
Bereavement	19	4·6	
Community relationships	44	10·8	36·2 per cent.
Pregnancy and Puerperium ⎱			
Infant feeding and care ⎰	17	4·2	*Difficulties*
Unmarried mother	24	5·9	*associated*
Infertility	3	0·7	*with reproductive*
Fear of pregnancy	4	1·0	*life*
Puberty	—	—	
Menopause	5	1·2	Total 53 cases
			13 per cent.

The sub-categories under 'CIRCUMSTANCES' were grouped into three sections as shown on the right, as they broadly indicate different types of work. The H.V.s, recording this work over one year, used the same categories, and as might be expected their score in the last group was high, and in the second group, low, the opposite holding for the M.S.W. This is discussed in Chapter 8.

It should be noted that cases were only entered under a heading if there were obvious reasons to associate the heading with the cause of the problem. A case would not be entered under 'Geriatric' simply because the age was over 65, but only if the effects of old age were a contributory cause of the presenting situation.

As cases were commonly entered in more than one category or sub-category, the total entries exceed the total number of cases in the series.

Fig. 8 shows that virtually all the problems were entered in one or more of the sub-categories under 'CIRCUMSTANCES' (99 per cent.). 'ILLNESS', as defined above, was a contributory factor in 56·5 per cent. of our cases, 'PERSONALITY' in 50·1 per cent. It is of interest that of the 409 situations referred, physical illness was estimated to be a contributory factor in only 56·5 per cent, and that in just over one half of the total the patient's personality was estimated to be factor in the presenting situation which brought the patient to the G.P.

Of the sub-categories under 'CIRCUMSTANCES', 'Housing', 'Geriatric', 'Occupation', and 'Finance' were the most heavily scored in the 'Social problems' group. ('Fatigue and worry' problems, 'Problem families', and those with 'Poor home management' were more commonly referred to the H.V.s).

36·2 per cent. of cases were entered in the 'Personal relationship difficulties' group, where the M.S.W. was commonly engaged on complex casework.

'Difficulties associated with reproductive life' was a territory more frequently trodden by the H.V.s, but occurring as a facet of the M.S.W.'s work at times, for example in work on unmarried mothers.

2. *Analysis of the action taken by the Medical Social Worker*

The action taken in each situation referred was looked at in retrospect in a similar way. Out of our experience certain categories of work done by the M.S.W. were built up. The 'Actions taken' fell into three broad categories:

a. Assessment of the patient and his problems; *interpretation* of the problem to him; *support*; and like assistance. These were services given by the M.S.W. to the patient without the use of other agencies.

b. Negotiations involving personal approaches by the M.S.W. to various social agencies, often in person, sometimes by telephone. The M.S.W. was acting here as a link between the patient and doctor on the one hand, and the Social Services on the other.

c. Purely administrative work, for example, arranging transport.

Fig. 9. *Action taken by the Medical Social Worker*

	Number of entries	Number of entries expressed as a percentage of a total series (409 cases)
1. *Assessment, interpretation or support*		
Assessement, no action necessary	11	2·7
Assessment of social factors for diagnosis	228	55·8
Interpretation	193	47·2
Listening, support, advice, informal medical education	360	88·0
Practical help personally given	18	4·4
2. *Negotiations involving personal approaches or case consultation by the M.S.W. re:*		
Work	82	20·0
Housing	97	23·7
Finance	57	13·9
Convalescence and holidays	23	5·6
Schooling	11	2·7
Recreation	18	4·4
Home care	56	13·7
Medical equipment	43	10·5
Illegitimate child	21	5·1
Miscellaneous	54	13·2
3. *Purely administrative work*		
Simple mobilization of a Social Service	1	0·2
Administrative arrangements for transport or appointments	14	3·4
Supply of medical equipment	2	0·5

381 cases were entered at least once in Group 1. 335 cases were entered at least once in Group 2. Only 17 cases were entered in Group 3. This partly reflects the policy of protecting the M.S.W. from routine administrative work, which was directed to the receptionist staff. But the low figure also illustrates how seldom the statutory Social Services can be effectively brought into action by a simple administrative request. In the complex types of social casework which make up much of this series personal contact between the M.S.W. and the social agency was commonly found necessary. This again highlights her function as a link with the Social Services.

Each of these categories was made up of the sub-categories indicated by our working experience. Cases were commonly entered in more than one category and sub-category and thus the entries exceed the number of cases in the series and the percentages exceed 100.

III. Factual recording by the Medical Social Worker

From the exacting work of categorizing the elements of patients' problems, and the action taken by the M.S.W., it was sometimes with a sense of relief that we turned to simple matters of fact. The M.S.W. recorded for each patient the following:

1. Age, sex, married state, and social class.

2. The number of surgery consultations with the M.S.W., and the number of home visits made.

3. The total time spent on each case; and the time-span of contact from referral to closure.

4. The number of M.S.W./G.P. consultations; and the number of M.S.W. consultations with 'other colleagues'.

5. The Social agencies contacted.

The consolidated figures from these records and the M.S.W.'s discussion of them can be found in Part Two, 2.

5. Did the Medical Social Worker save General Practitioners time?

Whether or not the M.S.W. saved G.P.–time is not easily measured in three years, as no account can be taken of the future benefits of the M.S.W.'s work in mapping out the social and emotional background of certain families and individuals in the practice, resolution of patient's problems, and improved knowledge on the part of the G.P. These reduce the time required for diagnosis and management of future or continuing situations. Nevertheless, some appreciation of time saved for G.P.s in this experiment, and also of the extra demands made on their time, can be attempted.

The latter is easier to assess and can be more obvious than the former. During the experiment the G.P.s have found time for case consultations with the M.S.W., some as regularly weekly routines, and some as *ad hoc* meetings, totalling about a half to one hour per week per G.P., sometimes more, sometimes less. Time was also given to occasional lunch-hour seminars, and to meetings in association with G.P.s and M.S.W.s from elsewhere. For the purpose of the experiment (as opposed to practice requirements) time was given to the completion of questionnaires, the writing of summaries, and to a few planning meetings early in the experiment. When averaged out over the three years, the time given is estimated to have cost each G.P. between one hour and one and a half hours per week. (To this has to be added a much larger contribution in time on the part of the G.P. responsible for planning and mounting the experiment.)

In return for this, some very time-consuming work has been taken off the G.P.'s shoulders by the M.S.W., in personal interviews with patients, in research into social conditions, and in mobilizing Social Services. The amount of this work which the G.P.s might have carried out themselves in the absence of the M.S.W. (as distinct from the amount which would not have been attempted) is suggested by the aggregated G.P.'s replies to Question 2 of the questionnaire. These indicate (Fig. 4) that in 34·2 per cent. of cases referred to the M.S.W., the work would have been covered by the G.P.s themselves in her absence (though in over half of these less adequately).

But the real saving of G.P.–time in the long term lies beyond this. Among the many obvious advantages of a diagnosis which is complete, not only in terms of organic disease, but also in terms of social and emotional factors, lies the considerable one of making future diagnosis and management easier and therefore quicker for the G.P. This is comparable to the situation of an experienced G.P. dealing with a family he has known well over many years, as compared with a locum dealing with the same family. Where social and emotional factors are at work, pinpointing the source of trouble comes more quickly and more surely to the former than the latter.

We agree completely with the comment made by a Dutch G.P. with experience similar to ours, to the effect that a complete social assessment, even when nothing can be done at the end of it to alter the state of affairs, puts the G.P. in a position to understand and manage future family crises better and more quickly than without it. It can be added that possession of a clearer social picture can increase both confidence and satisfaction for the G.P. A direct comparison can be made with the continuing care of patients for whom it has been possible to carry out a complete 'base-line' physical examination at the first contact.

Lastly, the methods and insights of the M.S.W. have to some extent rubbed off on our shoulders, and the shoulders of our staff. If this were consciously extended to better contact between medical and M.S.W. students in training; and to the involvement of M.S.W.s in the teaching of medical students and G.P. postgraduates, it should assist the G.P. in making social and emotional assessment for himself, and in identifying more surely and quickly these factors in the causation of symptoms.

It can be concluded that whereas the G.P.s taking part in this experiment have had to find time of the order of one to one and a half hours per week, the ultimate saving of time by the introduction of medicosocial help in general practice is likely to save G.P. time far in excess of this figure. Linked with this is a reduction of frustrations and doubts due to incomplete social and emotional diagnosis.

6. Estimates of need for medicosocial work in general practice

Although the need for medicosocial help in general practice is obvious, it is not easy to make a factual estimate of its extent. The boundaries of the work which an individual social worker may undertake vary with her training and experience, and this makes direct comparison of past and current experiments uncertain.

The role of M.S.W.s in the U.K. has undergone a revolution in recent years, and training still varies to some extent from centre to centre. But M.S.W.s., and perhaps other caseworkers, are among those best fitted by their training to make a true estimate of the unmet need themselves, if prepared to work within general practice.

The need may vary from area to area in quantity and quality. But we see the need as an intrinsic element in any domiciliary medical care.

Any attempt at surveying the need in a practice will also be dependent on the G.P.'s detection of situations calling for medicosocial help, and this in turn, depends on their attitudes and horizons; and their experience of working with social workers. As in so many areas of medical care, the more that is looked for, the more that is found; our experience is that in the present state of domiciliary care this is not an expression of Parkinson's Law, but of very real concealed need.

Opinions on the size of the unmet need have been expressed by others. Backett, Maybin, and Dudgeon in 1955, in a total survey of a small single-handed practice, concluded that '. . . one full-time and suitably trained worker might do the social work of a general practice of this type with a registered population of 4000', but the training of the social worker involved was not described in detail. Ignoring variables, this would imply a need for between three and four full-time social workers in a group practice of 14,400 patients, our setting in this experiment.

Joan Collins (3) attempted to estimate the concealed need in the group practice population on which she was working, at the end of her period of attachment, by a questionnaire to a 5 per cent. sample of the practice. Among those replying (80 per cent.) she estimated that 34 patients needed social help, but only 18 had obtained it, implying that only about half the patients in need of social help had in fact received it from herself or other sources during the course of the experiment.

The still current experiment at Nijmegen, Holland, referred to on p. 19, accepted 400 cases in need of social work from three general practices in sixteen months. From the fact that one of the three practitioners referred less than the two others, and that all three were new to this sort of case selection, it was deduced that this substantially underestimated the total need; the opinion was expressed that more cases of need came to light as experience in identifying them increased. On the other hand it is unknown how many of the 400 cases referred represented backlog, i.e. accumulated work from situations arising before the current period, and the figure cannot be taken to represent a continuing load. Of the 400, the social worker's accepted load was only 68 cases in one year.

It is interesting to speculate what the true need of the three practices was in terms of social worker help. If as much as half of the cases referred were taken as backlog (an improbably high figure) 200 cases a year would be the minimum demand. If 68 cases is one social worker's load, then the three practices would, at a *minimum* estimate, need three social workers to cover the ground.

In the present experiment, 409 cases were referred to the M.S.W. in three years. This caseload proved to be maximal and was probably excessive. Demand for her services was always in excess of supply, and it was difficult to limit acceptances.

The series of 409 cases was drawn from a practice of 14,400 potential patients, and was composed of a highly selected group whose problems demanded, aside from special skill, a large amount of time spent on them.

In attempting to estimate the unmet need for medicosocial care in the practice, certain factors can be measured from our figures. Those cases in which the G.P.s judged that the work done by the

M.S.W. had made 'no useful contribution' (21); and those cases in which the G.P.s judged that the work could have been done equally well by the existing Social Services (77); the existing surgery staff (14), or by other helpers (1), may reasonably be deducted from the figure of 409 cases to give an estimate of the true need.[1]

The figure thus arrived at is 296 *cases of need in three years*, and this might be taken as a *minimum estimate* for the group practice. We have no measure of the cases in need of help which we as G.P.s may have failed to identify; and no measure of the cases we would have referred to the M.S.W., had she been able to accept a bigger load. It is certain however that the numbers in the last category were considerable.

It should also be remembered that for two out of the three years of the experiment two H.V.s were attached to the practice and were taking regular social work referred from the G.P.s in addition to our referrals to the M.S.W.

These facts illustrate the size of the medicosocial problem in general practice, and are in accord with the estimates of social and emotional disability in general practice quoted above.

The necessity for more accurate estimates of unmet need for medicosocial help in general practice

An estimate of the true need arising per year, per unit number of the population, is badly needed if integrated work between G.P.s and social workers is to be developed. Total surveys of a patient population are unlikely to be helpful; it is not possible to assess patients' difficulties without subsequently providing help; and also a total survey of a population would be likely to leave many problems unreported. Patients present problems at the time of need, or in crises, and may conceal personal difficulties at other times. The most likely way of making an exhaustive estimate may be by a combined G.P. and M.S.W. team, where the G.P.s are skilled in identification, and the M.S.W. strength is sufficient to screen all evident and suspected problems. Clear-cut definition of the type of problems

1. Those cases in which the G.P.s judged they could have done the work equally well are omitted from the calculation, because in the present time-short setting of general practice it is unlikely that the work would in fact have been done by the G.P. Aside from this, it can be held that the G.P. is better employed on clinical work, which only he can carry out.

looked for would be required and some means of excluding 'backlog', i.e. problems arising from situations existing before the period of the assessment.

7. The siting of a Medical Social Worker in a group practice

It should be asked in the light of our experience whether the concept of a M.S.W. working within a group practice is sound. Leaving aside for the present questions of supply and demand, there are two points to answer: 'Does a Medical Social Worker in a group practice help the General Practitioner in the provision of overall medical care?', and 'Is a group practice a good contact point for the Medical Social Worker with patients in need of her services?'.

1. Does a Medical Social Worker in a group practice help the General Practitioner in the provision of overall medical care?

From the standpoint of medical practice we are in no doubt that the attachment of a M.S.W. to the practice has improved the service we offer. This is shown in the figures in Chapter 4. She has contributed in an area where our service under present conditions is perforce often inadequate; and this is an area in domiciliary practice which has been under-estimated in size and importance. Secondly we feel that her presence with us as a member of the practice in the same way that a partner, assistant, or nurse becomes a member of the practice, has been significant. There are four main reasons for this.

a. Communication
Problems of communication are formidable in general practice. The limits of communication outside the group practice team are soon met on grounds of time and accessibility. (Communication within the practice is demanding enough.) Written messages and telephone calls—even when they reach the right people—are far inferior to verbal exchanges when dealing with personal problems.

The great advantage of having a partner, an assistant, or an attached district nurse, working in the same building applies no less to co-operation with a M.S.W. Out of close and frequent co-operation comes mutual knowledge of personality, habits, and attitudes, and removal of semantic difficulties. Once the G.P. and M.S.W. have learnt to talk the same language, and are 'teamed up', efficiency rises in this context as it does between obstetrician and midwife, or surgeon and anaesthetist. It is one thing to ask help from an outside social worker on a case and hope to keep contact with her, and quite another to ask it of a member of the group, who knows one's methods, abilities, and limitations, has experience of the practice as a whole, and is certain to be available from day to day to co-ordinate progress.

Figs. 25 and 26 in Part Two, further illustrate the size of the G.P.s communication problem with the Social Services.

b. Acceptance by patients

If the G.P.–M.S.W.–Patient triangular relationship is to be of any use, patients must accept that their confidences to their doctor will be shared by the M.S.W., and vice versa. Not every patient can accept this initially, though once established the triangular relationship has given no difficulty in this experiment. A proposal to bring a third party into the doctor–patient relationship and into the patients' personal problems is more acceptable if the third party is a member of the practice team, and can truly be introduced, as a partner would be, as a confidential second opinion. Many patients are, however unreasonably, chary of exposing their personal affairs to officers of the Social Services, often believing that their confidences will not necessarily remain with the officer himself.

These considerations do not apply to every case referred, but they apply to many in the greatest need.

c. The professional independence of the Medical Social Worker

In this experiment the M.S.W. has been as professionally independent as the G.P.s she was working with. She has had to make no reports on her work to a higher authority; and her daily routine has been shaped solely by the heavy demands of the work. This has been a point of envy on the part of our two H.V.s, who have felt hampered by having to make returns to the Local Health Authority on their day to day work, in great detail, and, as they feel, in a framework not realistically related to what they were doing. We feel this is an important point. If supervision is required at all, it must be by those who thoroughly understand general practice, its pressures, and its needs. It is doubtful if obligatory returns of work done in detail are ever likely to do more than consume working time and cause frustrations. Recording of work for a specific research project, which can be seen to be of value by the recorders, is in a different category.

d. The indivisibility of medical and social illness

The essence of general practice is that it is holistic medicine. All factors which contribute to disability, whether physical, social, or emotional, are forced upon the G.P. in making diagnoses and providing care, whether he likes it or not. Very commonly these factors are interdependent and inseparable, and taking account of all three together is a day to day necessity for him.

At the same time he cannot expect to cover all the social casework required, or to spend time on co-ordinating the contributions of Social Service departments, in addition to covering the clinical medicine for his patients.

Some social problems which form a facet of a family's overall care can be referred as an isolated piece of work to a Social Service department with success. Others, often complex problems which are vital to patients' disability, cannot.

Example. A single girl of 19 working as a shop assistant presented with recurrent syncopal attacks. There was commonly a dramatic element, in that they occurred in the street, or while working in the crowded store, and the voice on the telephone summoning the G.P. urgently usually conveyed the anxiety and excitement of the bystanders. An hysterical basis for the attacks was the G.P.'s first diagnostic choice, but there was a history of suspected epilepsy in the girl's father, and of syncopal attacks in her own childhood. The Neurologist however, found no positive evidence of epilepsy. An element of doubt remained.

She continued to suffer attacks and to frequent the surgery; and she lost job after job because of her disability. No progress was made in control of the attacks in spite of frequent discussions with her G.P. It became evident that relationships at home were difficult and that she herself was emotionally immature though not un-intelligent. Incorporation of the M.S.W. into the problem produced a full social history, and the home stresses were evaluated for all three people involved—the patient, the G.P., and the M.S.W. Her parents' marriage had always been difficult and her father was then living away from home. Her mother had a close relationship with her but had a dominant personality. The girl had drifted into an engagement with a boy who lodged with the family, but she had now lost interest and wanted to break with him, against family advice. She had become emotionally involved with a young married man whose marriage was breaking down. During this period the patient continued to discuss her situation with both M.S.W. and G.P. separately, and frequent brief discussions between the latter were essential in fitting together the parts of the picture as it was revealed, and as it changed; and in order to keep the management of the case moving along a single line of thought.

It is in this respect that work with the M.S.W. in the practice team differed so greatly from referral of cases to, say, a Psychiatrist, a Child Guidance Clinic, or a Social Service department, where professional contact is limited to an initial letter from the G.P. and the final report from the specialist. Often enough the G.P. and the others involved in handling the case reach differing conclusions, each possibly incomplete, and an unco-ordinated and unsatisfactory management of the problem results. To work with the 'triangular' relationship of patient, G.P., and third party, the G.P. and the third party must have a good working knowledge of each other, and continuing frequent contact. Otherwise patients become involved in two or more isolated therapeutic relationships and may be confused by conflicting attitudes and interpretations.

Over some weeks the girl gained insight into her complaint. Her personal problems were helped, and she was found a new job. The fainting attacks became less frequent and finally stopped, and before long she was at work well, and independent of her G.P. and the M.S.W. About a year later she married her original fiance and at the time of writing is having her first child. She has had no syncopal attacks for eighteen months and can discuss her past difficulties without embarrassment.

This type of case is unsuitable for a busy psychiatric out-patients department, or a psychiatric ward handling the major psychoses. It is best handled within the practice team and this becomes possible for the most complex situations when the appropriate skilled help and the time are available.

It is here that for the G.P., a professional colleague in the team is of greater value than any array of Social Service departments, however co-operative, and however efficient in themselves.

2.   Is a group practice a good contact point for the Medical Social Worker with patients in need of her services?

Everyone has a G.P. and on average everyone sees him about four times a year. This does not mean that everyone sees his G.P., nor does it mean that every social or emotional problem is presented to him. But bearing in mind the close association of medical, social, and emotional problems, and the frequency of contact between patient and G.P., the G.P. is better placed than anyone else in the community, (schoolmasters might challenge this for children) to identify early signs of trouble, and bring in M.S.W. help at that point. Indeed he has a growing obligation to do so, and his teachers have a growing obligation to train him to do it.

Continuity of care

The continuity of care of patients and families over years by a G.P. has a built-in efficiency factor. His accumulated knowledge of them individually and in family groups, and of their environment, is one of the things which make it possible, even with present day lists of patients, to manage a practice in the time available. (This does not imply that his knowledge of all his patients is exhaustive.) The same consideration suggests that maximum effect, for the time spent by a M.S.W. in the community, is likely to be achieved when she has spent long enough working on a practice population to know something about many of its members. The more closely she applies herself to the practice community, the more commonly is knowledge of one situation found to be valuable in another, and the more the work she has done reduces the future load. Further, in a group practice, knowledge of personalities and social facts are often available from others in the practice and form an invaluable common pool of background knowledge.

A disadvantage of Medical Social Worker attachment to a practice

Considerations of current supply and demand of M.S.W.s may make some of the comments in this chapter unrealistic. But the present concern is to study the effects on general medical and medicosocial practice when integrated, not to make administrative policy.

One of the problems which arose was the isolation of our M.S.W.

from others of her profession. This was largely due to the isolation of the area, and to the fact that for a large part of the three-year appointment her nearest professional colleagues were forty miles away. Nevertheless, there would be an intrinsic factor of isolation in the situation of attachment to any group practice, even if sited in a city, which is not present in hospital work. One suggested way of overcoming this is the creation of joint appointments, in which a M.S.W. would divide her time between a Local Health Authority or Hospital Service, and a group practice, or a group of single-handed practitioners. Provided there is continuity over a long enough period, and that sufficient time is allotted to general practice work to make the M.S.W. a working member of the practice or practices to which she is attached, this could be a useful method. In this experiment it can be said that the M.S.W. has been available to *each* G.P., in round terms, at the rate of one day a week, and 'sufficient time' would need to be interpreted in this sort of measure. An attachment to a *group* practice for one day a week for instance is not likely to provide sufficient experience of working together to generate a worthwhile combined attack on the large volume of medicosocial need which exists.

How great the difficulties of working with two such different organizations as a Local Health Authority and a group practice might be would have to be found by trial. In this context, the professional freedom of the M.S.W. mentioned above might be jeopardized.

8. The Medical Social Worker and the Health Visitors

The M.S.W. was attached to the practice for three years. During the second and third years two H.V.s were also attached, by courtesy of the Medical Officer of Health for Devon; that is they accepted the patients of the practice as the community for which they were responsible, in place of a geographical area, and became very much members of the practice team. In order to make integration with partners as close as possible, each H.V. was attached to three G.P.s and their practices.[1]

We have been able to draw some conclusions from our experience of working with a M.S.W. and two H.V.s in the practice. The first is that there was more than enough work for all three; all were pressed by claims on their services. Secondly, the M.S.W. and the H.V.s in the main carried out very different work, but there was an area of overlap in the work which might be carried by either.

The type of work taken on by the Health Visitors

The Medical Officer of Health attached the two H.V.s to the practice with an open brief, except for certain duties to be carried out for the Local Health Authority outside and inside the work of the group practice. Their work in the practice evolved by a system of trial and error. By 1966 each H.V. was spending approximately one-third of her working time in the clinics of the practice and Local Health Authority referred to below; and two-thirds in dealing with individual

1. The number of G.P.s working with each H.V. varied at times for several reasons; but the principle was followed that the patient population taken on by each H.V. was approximately half the practice total, and they were the patients of the doctors to whom she was attached.

patient's problems, referred to her by the G.P.s of the practice or reaching her by direct approach from patients themselves.

Clinics conducted in the surgery on practice patients include a weekly Well Baby and Immunisation Clinic, Ante-Natal and Post-Natal Clinics twice weekly, a fortnightly Hearing Test Clinic for infants at nine months, and an open afternoon when mothers and babies can come for discussion of problems with the H.V.s. Extension of the Well Baby Clinic to all pre-school children is imminent and will involve the H.V.s in a major role so that the time spent in this work may increase.

The H.V.s also serve on Local Health Authority Clinics for child welfare, for ante-natal health education and relaxation classes, and one runs a Mothers' Club in an outlying area. There are also light and occasional duties in school clinics and elsewhere.

Approximately two-thirds of the H.V.'s working time has been spent on individual patient's problems. In one twelve-month period two H.V.s together dealt with 363 such problems. 170 were referred by the G.P.s, and 189 reached the H.V. by direct approach from the patients after previous contact at clinics or through the G.P. The majority of the latter were mother and baby problems, such as feeding difficulties, crises of confidence in young mothers after leaving the Obstetric Unit, and so on. Four cases were referred from other sources.

The content of the work done in this series of 363 referred case problems is looked at more closely below and compared with the M.S.W.'s load.

In the present state of our experience therefore we see the H.V.'s role as follows:

1. In the type of clinics referred to above.

2. In dealing with individual patient problems. It is in this sector that we have found some overlap with the M.S.W.'s work.

3. A developing role in planned screening procedures on certain groups of the practice population.

Most of this work demands training based on nursing and midwifery.

Attachment of the H.V.s to the group practice has brought for the first time teamwork between G.P. and H.V. on the same group of patients. We have found this to be of the greatest value; the H.V.s themselves are equally enthusiastic about the benefits of the system.

The Medical Social Worker's work in comparison

In contrast to the H.V.s, the M.S.W.'s work has been centred on medicosocial problems, many of which are complex, and many of which involve personal relationship difficulties, or problems of insight and attitude. This work and the associated work of contacting social agencies and steering patients through the maze of social services has been carried out on a highly selected group of cases which require a high proportion of time per case. It demands freedom from frequent interruptions, and from the need to handle large numbers of patients quickly. The relevant training is essentially in social casework, with background knowledge of the social and behavioural sciences; it also requires a professional knowledge of all social agencies, statutory and voluntary, local and distant, which can be mobilized in the service of individual patients, and ability to bring them into play effectively. H.V.s are not trained in depth for this type of work, and it is our impression that they could not find the time to deal with it if their present work-load is continued. The two contributions are distinct, and our experience leads us to think that it is doubtful wisdom to think in terms of one individual attempting to cover both, however trained. Still worse is the confusion of the two roles. It would be as sensible to ask our M.S.W. to take responsibility for breast-feeding problems or ante-natal health education, as it would be to ask the H.V. to take on complex inter-personal relationship problems without training for it.

It may be useful here to refer back, in a wider context, to the three basic needs in a group practice team:

1. Receptionist and secretarial work.

2. Help requiring a nurse's training, extending from nursing procedures, through midwifery, to the work of H.V.s. (Some procedures carried out by nurses might be as well done by technicians.)

3. Medicosocial casework of high calibre. The need here is great because the incidence of this type of work is great in general practice and it is here that G.P.s are least trained and least assisted.

Where the Medical Social Worker and Health Visitor may overlap

All medicosocial problems are not complex and many are well dealt with by the G.P. himself, the H.V., the District Nurse, and others. Such problems still call for more than administrative competence in that they involve human problems calling for individual solutions, and for persistence in seeing the work through to the best interest of the patient. A great deal more is involved than simple referral to a social agency.

Example. A recently widowed woman in her seventies with a past history of minor behavioural abnormalities and living alone in her own house, began reacting to her difficulties by making impossible demands for help on her neighbours at all hours of the day and night. For personal reasons her children, living elsewhere, would not help or take responsibility for her. Her demands on her G.P. were frequent and often at night, and there was commonly nothing of lasting importance that he could do on arrival; often she would call for a visit, and be out when he arrived. She refused admission to a Geriatric Unit and would make no plan for adapting to her limited capacities. The police became involved because of complaints by neighbours.

The H.V. was enlisted and transformed the scene. She co-opted the goodwill of some of the neighbours. She succeeded in befriending the patient, by initially helping with undone household chores, and cooking her a meal. Help in the house was arranged and volunteers found to visit her. The H.V.'s supportive follow-up visits were of greater use than the G.P.'s whose role was rightly reduced to the initial physical and emotional diagnosis and the use of simple sedation as required.

This is typical of work which is best carried out by someone working closely with the G.P., but which is not of a complexity to require a M.S.W.'s casework training.

Aptitude

In comparing the roles of M.S.W. and H.V. and relating them to their training, it is evident that individual interests and aptitudes for social work in medical care play a part in determining the size of the 'overlap area' of the M.S.W.'s and H.V.'s areas of work. Everyone caring for patients carries out 'casework' in some degree. It is the complexity of the situation which demands different degrees of skill and training. An individual with natural aptitude and interest in personal problems, whether trained as a nurse, health visitor, medical

Fig. 10. *Pattern of work done by both Health Visitors over twelve months on 363 cases referred to them.*

	Percentage of total cases entered
Assessment, Interpretation, Support	
Assessment. No action necessary	1·1
Assessment of social factors for diagnosis	5·0
Interpretation	3·6
Listening, support, advice, informal medical education	70·2
Practical help personally given	5·5
Negotiations involving personal approaches or case-consultation re:	
Work	0·3
Housing	3·9
Finance	4·4
Convalescence/holidays	—
Schooling	1·4
Recreation	0·6
Home care	2·5
Medical equipment	1·7
Work related to nursing midwifery	
Collection of pathological specimen	0·8
Supervision of medical régime	5·2
Infant feeding or care	31·7
Miscellaneous	1·1
Administrative work	
Simple mobilization of Social Services	8·3
Administrative arrangements (clinic appointment, transport, etc.)	6·6
Supply of medical equipment	1·4

social worker, or a doctor, can go further than one whose talents are for different work. Generalizations about what type of work can be carried by the H.V. and what cannot, need to be seen with this in mind.

The pattern of work done by the two Health Visitors in this experiment

The two H.V.s recorded the work done on individual case problems referred to them for twelve months and results are shown in Fig. 10. This gives some information of the role they played in this sector of the work. The H.V.s used the same categories as the M.S.W. in recording their work, entering each case in the appropriate category or categories (one or more entries for each case, according to the action or actions taken). The aggregated figures for both H.V.s are shown.

It is evident that a supportive advisory or educational role was played in over 70 per cent. of the cases dealt with; and that the other major role was in managing problems of infant feeding and care. Liaison work with various social agencies takes a lesser, but useful, place. Comparison with the work done by the M.S.W. in her series of cases (Fig. 9, p. 30) shows that she had no work in the third category above, and much heavier commitments in the first two.

[Further light can be thrown on the 'area of overlap' with the M.S.W. by examining those cases in the M.S.W. series which the G.P.s in retrospect felt could have been managed equally well by the H.V. (75 cases). (See Fig. 6, p. 24.) These are compared in Fig. 11 with cases which the G.P.s judged the H.V. could *not* have managed the problem (101 cases). If these cases are traced in the tables of 'The nature of the problem', as assessed by the M.S.W., significant differences are found and these are shown in Fig. 11.

Housing and geriatric problems appear commonly where the G.P.s felt that the H.V.s could have dealt with the situation as well

Fig. 11. *From the series of cases referred to M.S.W.*

	Cases recorded suitable for H.V. (75 cases) Percentage of the 75 cases	*Cases recorded unsuitable for H.V. (101 cases) Percentage of the 101 cases*
Housing	34·7	19·8
Geriatric	30·7	17·8
Finance	10·7	22·8

as the M.S.W., but the reverse is shown in problems of finance. This may be a pointer in selecting future referrals for H.V. or M.S.W.]

Complexity in casework often depends on the personality or personalities of the patients involved. This is indicated by comparing the opinions of the M.S.W. on the one hand, and the two H.V.s on the other, in recording their respective series of cases. Using the same terminology and categories, each was asked to identify the aetiological factors contributing to the problems they were referred. In her series the M.S.W. considered the patient's personality to be an aetiological factor in a little over 50 per cent. of the total series. By comparison the two H.V.s recorded that the personality of the patient was an aetiological factor in only 5·5 per cent. of their series. This is shown graphically in Fig. 12 below.

It is apparent that the number of cases entered in the *Illness* and *Circumstances* categories were broadly similar in either series, 'circumstances' of one sort or another being reckoned causative to the problem in nearly all cases of both series. The striking difference is in the rating of *Personality* as a factor referred to above. This is taken to reflect the frequency with which personality difficulties underlie the more complex problems, for which the M.S.W. was selected by the G.P., rather than the H.V.

It must be remembered in looking at these figures that three different individuals with different training backgrounds were here recording not facts, but factors in the problem as they saw them; and that the cases in each series were selected by the G.P.s for the M.S.W. or the H.V.

Fig. 12

M.S.W. series 409 cases	Percentage of total cases entered in each group		H.V. series 363 cases	Percentage of total cases entered in each group
	56·5	Illness		39·4
	50·1	Personality		5·5
	99·0	Circumstances		83·7

9. Conclusions

Medical teaching is still reticent about the social and emotional sources of illness. Experience in general practice perforce brings some understanding of their importance, but it is not surprising that this area of medical care can remain weak. This is a serious defect, since possibly as many as a half of the situations presenting to G.P.s have social or emotional factors of significance to diagnosis or management, and for the doctor of first contact their recognition is a main function. Some of these situations originate mainly or wholly in socio-emotional difficulties unrelated to physical disease; some are of great complexity.

G.P.s are also committed to the management of these situations, as they form part of the pattern of many physical illnesses, and cannot be separated from them. Unfortunately the bias of medical training towards physical disease may lead to underestimation of the time and skill required for the social and emotional elements in the whole; or they may be completely overlooked through lack of awareness.

The proper cover of this element of domiciliary medicine needs attention. Even if G.P.s are in future educationally better equipped for it, they cannot be expected to handle it unaided as well as to keep abreast of their rapidly changing and expanding clinical responsibilities. The existing Social Service departments cannot meet the need for intimate day to day help with the social and emotional elements in sick people. The work needs to be closely correlated with the G.P.s diagnostic screening, and continuing care. And in the many instances in which existing social services have a role to play, they need to be mobilised and correlated by someone other than the G.P. himself. This is illustrated in Figs. 25 and 26, Part Two, 9, pp. 101–102.

This report describes one way of approaching the problem: by the siting of a M.S.W. in a group practice. It demonstrates that she has worked successfully in this practice; the service offered by its G.P.s has been usefully extended, and the M.S.W. has shown how large her contribution can be in an important and currently neglected area of domiciliary care. The preventive factor in the work is noted. It is clear that the G.P.s have been saved time on cases with complex social and emotional features during the experiment; and armed with new background knowledge of families and individuals of importance to future diagnosis and management, this time-saving element will continue to bear fruit in the future.

As a site for the M.S.W. the practice has put her directly in touch with patients in their normal environments; it has given her an opportunity to work in continuity with families and individuals and to approach socio-emotional problems at an early stage in their development. Increased knowledge of her subject is afforded to all members of the practice team.

The working partnership of G.P.s and M.S.W. has provided a service which the realities of domiciliary care demand, and which cannot be given by G.P.s or Social Service departments in relative isolation from each other.

The experiment has been a demanding one on the M.S.W., working not only in isolation from her professional colleagues, but also in the unfamiliar setting of general practice, where no precedent or working organization existed. Future schemes should limit the caseload the M.S.W. is expected to carry.

We recognize the size of the socio-emotional problem in general practice but have no measure of the *total* unmet need. We have however been able to make a *minimum* estimate of need for this practice.

Using a system of referral of cases to the M.S.W. as the G.P.s saw need, we have made retrospective analysis of the aetiological factors in the problems referred, and of the M.S.W.'s actions necessary to meet the need.

Health Visitors

We have had the opportunity of having two H.V.s working in the practice, in addition to the M.S.W. and we have been able to indicate their respective fields of work as it has developed here. There has been more than enough work for the M.S.W. and both H.V.s, and all three have been hard pressed in their own spheres.

The nature of the Medical Social Worker's contribution

The M.S.W.'s chief contributions to the work of the practice in the eyes of the G.P.s concerned have been:

1. Her casework skill in dealing with the more complex social and emotional situations arising in the course of their work.

2. Her knowledge of the whole range of available social services, and her skill in bringing them promptly and effectively into play.

To these may be added:

3. Her influence on all members of the group practice in increasing their awareness of her subject.

Future needs in general practice

There is little available information on the incidence of medicosocial problems requiring skilled help in general practice. A co-ordinated study to estimate this in a variety of areas of the country is a necessary step towards any planned attempt to meet the need generally. Such a study should be undertaken. Its results should influence future training programmes, and the future pattern of the domiciliary medical team.

It is not for us to say how these needs are to be met from the various available sources. But we put forward from our experience the following considerations:

1. The area of need is large and its full extent as yet unmeasured.

2. The casework skill of the M.S.W. in this experiment has been her greatest contribution and we see in the lack of this our greatest need. Casework in a general practice setting must be of a high standard, not necessarily specialized, but sufficiently orientated to medicine for mutual understanding and co-operation between caseworker and G.P.

3. G.P.s, M.S.W.s, and others must work sufficiently closely in time and space to develop mutual insight and easy frequent communication.

4. G.P.s, M.S.W.s, H.V.s, and nurses should train together in the period of in-service or post-graduate training. M.S.W.s have an

important contribution to make to post-graduate medical education for general practice.

5. The development of medicosocial care by the introduction of suitably selected and trained personnel into the general practice of the future is likely to be more economical and more effective than equivalent investment in developing more social service departments working in relative isolation from general practice. General practice is a natural field for early identification of social and emotional difficulties.

PART TWO

Report by E. M. Fairbairn

1. The General Practitioner setting

Introduction

In this experiment we have been concerned to find out whether an M.S.W. introduced into a large group practice in a country area could fit in and make a contribution. The foregoing chapters describe the results from the G.P.'s point of view. This part of the report considers the significant points as seen by the social worker.

In hospital one is only in touch with a small proportion of the population. A study carried out in North Carolina in 1961 on *The Ecology of Medical Care* (**16**) neatly illustrates this point. Of 1,000 population in any month, the writers found that 750 would have some ailment, 250 would consult their doctor, 9 would be hospitalized, 5 would require a specialist's opinion, and 1 would go on to a university centre for fuller investigation!

The G.P. is a point of first contact. The social worker working with him should be in a strong position to reach medicosocial problems at source, to help before troubles reach crisis point. Patient, G.P., and specialist services would all benefit.

In our study the doctors judged that in 140 cases out of the 409, the M.S.W. had had a prophylactic value.

I found that, once there was an M.S.W. service available, the partners referred patients at an earlier stage, when there was more chance of doing constructive work. In the early referrals we had worked through a depressing backlog of hard cases which had been a trial and perplexity to the doctors for too long. With practice, I became surer in assessing which patients could use help and move forward, and the doctors became much more sophisticated in their expectations of the service. Where at first they would ask for a specific treatment service—say a job or house to be supplied for the patient, they later recognized that social problems are often complex, that the patient's personality and attitude might be factors causing him to need help, where someone else would have got their own job or house unaided. In a similar project in a Dutch practice in Nijmegen, the same change in referral was noted—where the partners had first asked for a specific service, later referrals were for a general social assessment.

For many patients a period in hospital is a strange episode in their lives—they are separated from their families and are lifted out of their everyday routine. At a time of serious accident or illness, one's feelings are often intensified, one is forced to face situations where one may normally just drift along. In such moments of crisis a social worker may help considerably in quite a short contact with her patient. Work in general practice is seldom like this. One is helping patients to live with situations which continue to be part of their lives—the handicapped child, the homebound patient, the lonely old lady. When one's entry into a situation has been at a point of crisis—unmarried motherhood or a sudden family flare-up, this first contact may well lead on to a continuing association with the family. One comes to know every member of the household and to be aware of the interaction between them and the way in which each is touched by any problem affecting one of the others.

Example. I worked with a housewife with many discontents—she found her neighbours difficult and unfriendly, and her employers not appreciative of her conscientious efforts. We were in touch for some time and during this period the family moved house, she changed her job and settled into a happier phase. Her young daughter was then coming on to adolescence and presented with fainting fits. Neurological investigation proved negative and I was asked to keep in touch. The little girl revealed some difficulty in school relationships and co-ordination with the school staff was indicated over career plans. When visiting I was intrigued at being addressed by name by a younger brother with whom I had had little direct contact, and claimed to admire his latest construction. The family took it for granted that I was concerned with all of them, just as their G.P. was.

Example. Another patient, a nervous middle-aged man with gastric troubles, had rehabilitation problems. Careful handling of both patient and employers was needed to help him back to work, but two years later he was still there. His wife then sought me out because of concern about their backward daughter who, at 24, had suddenly realized that her job was boring and that she had no friends, and might be left stranded if her parents died! It was possible to draw her into a club run by the county staff where she would not be outstripped by brighter companions, and where the staff should give her parents some support in caring for this handicapped girl.

There is great satisfaction in coming to know one's community so well. One may not keep in regular touch because there are others with more urgent claims, but patients return and seek one out for relatives and friends if one's help has been of value.

The second factor which makes general practice a good setting is the relationship between G.P. and patient and the G.P.'s understanding of his patients.

I was surprised to see the way in which patients addressed their doctor as man to man, stated their symptoms, and often added suggestions as to treatment! I had never thought of hospital patients as being cowed, but they never behaved in quite this way. The G.P.'s reactions were the next surprise—when asked for an opinion, they were clear and decisive and assumed full responsibility. A doctor who is one of a team of about twenty on a professorial unit is in a different position and it is often difficult for any doctor to give firm estimates, but lack of decision or the difference of opinion which can rise between doctors in such units can upset the patient considerably.

Length of contact and familiarity with the home and neighbourhood has a lot to do with the easy relationship between the G.P. and his patients. This is a long-established practice in a country area. The doctors are held in high regard by their patients and it is natural for them to be consulted on many concerns which at first sight have little connexion with physical illness. The World Health Organisation definition mentions three elements in the service the G.P. offers to his patients—accessibility, continuity, and a comprehensive approach to patient care. I was impressed by the G.P.'s broad interpretation of medical care, apparently regarding the total well-being of patients as their relevant concern. In face of this, however, I was not sure where I fitted in and whether there was need for a social worker in general practice. At the end of three years, I am certain there is a need—I could only tackle a small part of the work the doctors wanted to refer.

Dr. David Morrell in his monograph on *The Art of General Practice* (9) describes the reaction of a young doctor entering general practice from hospital:

Another alarming result of the accessibility of the general practitioner is the wide variety of problems on which he is expected to give advice. These reach far beyond the limits of medicine as taught in medical school. Such subjects as the behaviour of children, adolescence, marriage, and the menopause receive but scant attention in the medical curriculum; divorce, house mortgage, and hire purchase debts are normally omitted altogether. Yet the general practitioner will be expected to have an opinion about all these problems and many others. He may feel that he is not only unqualified to deal with such matters, but that they are outside of his terms of service and that it is unreasonable for his patients to make these demands on him.

He then makes the point that the doctor who fails to adapt to these needs may miss good opportunities of gaining insight into the lives of his patients. A M.S.W. can guide him in these fields.

2. The nature of the M.S.W.'s contribution

An aid to assessment

To a M.S.W., the G.P.'s greater awareness of the social aspects of their patients' problems can be a challenge but also an opportunity. The G.P. may have his own views on the social diagnosis and treatment, founded on a much longer acquaintance with the families than a newly arrived social worker can have, but a M.S.W.s awareness of the attitudes and behaviour of sick people is trained to a higher degree than that of a doctor and this should help her to make much clearer assessments in this sphere. She can recognize the range of reactions which a human being employs to come to terms with each new situation, showing a fighting spirit or becoming depressed and dependent, and so on.

I do not mean to suggest that any patient going through such experiences will need social support to keep going—many adapt and come to terms with their situations. I suggest, however, that if a G.P. is aware of these factors he will have an alertness and will be more likely to note any patient's need for help and make it easier for him to express it, which is half the battle in finding the treatment, and the essence of preventive medicine. It is important too, for doctors and all others in helping professions to develop this awareness, because it is they who must put the patient in touch with social help. Every patient has a G.P. but not every patient has or needs a social worker. If the G.P. does not develop this awareness and obtain the right help the patient may well fall more heavily on him, becoming chronically depressive or hypochondriac. Dr. John Horder spoke of this in a memorial lecture given in 1966 on *The Role of the General Practitioner in Psychological Medicine* (**17**):

Turning to secondary prevention—stopping or limiting disorders through early treatment—we are on firmer and more familiar ground. We can do this now for episodes of depressive illness by using the right drugs at the right time. But even more commonly—perhaps more than once a day, we see anxious people with physical symptoms for which there is no primary physical cause. How we handle them may decide whether they recover quickly or embark on a long career of invalidism. We will all have seen middle-aged women, dissatisfied and unhappy, who have gone from doctor to doctor and had unnecessary investigations, treatments, and even operations, because some general practitioner lacked either the perception or the courage to see what was happening and protect them from themselves and other doctors.

Speaking at a conference on community care, Dame Eileen Younghusband said that we still needed to identify the vulnerable groups in our society, the types of situation which are likely to produce strain. We can then be alert to help at thee arliest moment and so save families from struggling alone with a situation to such a point of deterioration that it may be too late to do much constructive work.

Vulnerability may be linked with periods of change in people's lives. When a child is leaving the shelter of home and going off to school, he is having to summon all his independence and his ability to give and take with other children. When a young couple marry, they are learning to adapt to each other, to establish their place in society, to rear a family, with all that this involves. And later on, when one partner dies, the other is left to readapt to life alone and to come to terms with old age. Other factors may be identified which can place stress upon people and make them vulnerable—illness and disablement, lack of a secure and loving home, and the social upheaval of modern society, the effects of two world wars and an industrial and housing situation which often requires men to pull up their roots and move off at the drop of a hat—which separates husbands from families, and the young from the older generation.

Interesting work has been done by a Dutch G.P., Dr. Huygen, (18) who is now President of the Dutch College of General Practitioners. For his teaching work with students planning to enter general practice, he kept records on patients' consultation rates and compared them with parallel records showing events going on in the household over the same period. He found that there was a correlation between periods of high consultation and periods of change in a

Fig. 13

Elements in problem	Percentage of each group		
	Married women aet 25–44 (63 cases)	Single adolescents aet 15–24 (35 cases)	Patients over 65 (114 cases)
Illness			
Yes	38·1	22·9	83·3
Personality			
Yes	66·7	60·0	29·8
Circumstances			
Schooling	4·8	2·9	—
Occupation	20·6	51·4	6·1
Housing	22·2	—	40·4
Finance	14·3	11·4	7·0
Miscellaneous	12·7	5·7	41·2
Fatigue and/or worry	12·7	—	4·4
Problem family	1·6	—	—
Poor home management	14·3	11·4	—
Geriatric	—	—	77·1
Relationship problems			
Adolescent difficulties	4·8	11·4	—
Marital differences	30·2	—	0·8
Parent–child differences	9·5	22·9	0·8
Relatives	14·3	—	4·4
Solitary living	—	2·9	2·6
Bereavement	—	—	7·9
Community relationships	27·0	11·4	2·6
Reproductive			
Pregnancy, puerperium, infant feeding and care	11·1	—	0·8
Unmarried mother	—	40·0	0·8
Infertility	1·6	—	—
Fear of pregnancy	1·6	2·9	—

Note. The number of entries made for each patient in the table is variable, depending on the factors contributing to the problems referred.

family, when a child was arriving, when the eldest son was leaving home, the months following a death.

We were interested to see the results of a comparative study of the incidence and variation of problems among the different age groups in our own project. The more that problems can be defined and their range and incidence plotted, the easier it will be for the G.P. to recognize such troubles. It should also help him to decide what type of ancillary help is most relevant for his patients. (See also Chapter 8.)

As in other studies, *Married women of child-bearing age* form a large group. They carry responsibility for the young family at this stage and their difficulties included the unhappy phenomenon of the depressed housewife. This is a complex problem and there are probably several causes. Housework in a modern labour-saving home may not offer sufficient interest to the woman who has had the stimulus and companionship of a job before marriage. After a break from such activity however, and intervening family responsibilities, she seems to need help in regaining self-confidence to venture into part-time work again or even in establishing friendly contacts with other young wives. More nursery or other facilities are required to give young mothers some break from responsibility, a chance to go on the occasional outing or shopping spree. Fig. 13 shows that this group commonly presented a Personality factor (66·7 per cent.) whereas Physical illness was less common (38·1 per cent.). They needed a good deal of help with Relationship problems. (Marital Difficulties 30·2 per cent.; Community relationships 27·0 per cent.; Relationships with relatives 14·3 per cent.; Parent–child relationships 9·5 per cent.).

The *Adolescents* are an important group. If one can work with skill and understanding at this stage there is more chance of achieving constructive progress before the patterns of personality and life have become too set. In contrast, time expended on vagrants or chronic alcoholics is relatively unproductive; by this stage the help one can offer can often only be palliative. Help with careers (Occupation 51·4 per cent.) and with Personality and Relationship problems, (Adolescent difficulties 11·4 per cent.; Parent–child difficulties 22·9 per cent.; Community relationships 11·4 per cent.) was needed here. Physical illness was less commonly a factor. There were a number of unmarried mothers in the group (40 per cent.).

We also looked at the *Geriatric group*. Here the need for social help was often related to problems arising out of Physical illness (83·3 per cent.) while Personality difficulties were less common (29·8 per cent.) Housing problems were common (40·4 per cent.).

Social problems

When I came to the practice, one question constantly recurred—'Which patients can you help?' There are three types of patient who are time-consuming for the G.P. and where a M.S.W.'s knowledge seems of particular relevance. In this practice concern for patients who still returned to surgery after examination and reassurance had led to this experiment. In Holland, G.P.s had speculated about the patient who remains ill, though the original organic trouble had been cleared up.

A M.S.W.'s training in social assessment can be of particular help where the problem presenting in the G.P.'s surgery springs not from physical illness but from primarily social difficulties. Work with these patients is often characterized by an air of tension and muddle—they are prone to call out their G.P. at short notice at any hour of day or night, and when he arrives those surrounding the patient seem incapable of helping him to bring calm, but seem instead to add to the difficulties. Normal reassurance and advice on medical care seem ineffective in reaching these patients' conditions. Where such troubles spring from personal difficulties and unhappy relationships, a M.S.W. should have the knowledge to identify the factors, and the skill to help.

Example. One of the families in the area had frequent cause to consult their doctor. The mother's health and nerves were poor, there were some difficulties over marriage matters, and the only child had been a poor feeder and was now having pains and nightmares following her start at school. Social inquiry revealed that the mother's own childhood had been unhappy and insecure. The marriage was a happy one but there were certain strains, partially related to the man's absorption in his trade and his 'foreign' wife's greater difficulty in fitting into the local scene. This was the background in which the only child, a healthy and appealing little girl was producing the symptoms mentioned. Child Guidance therapy was arranged for her but I continued to see the mother as the contact was well established. Her understanding has helped her to relax with her little girl whose obvious improvement has cheered the mother enormously. This patient will probably always be vulnerable, but the social referral has helped to clarify the situation.

There are other patients who can prove very time-consuming and the young trainee just entering general practice is fair game for them. *These are the socially inadequate who present with long and confused histories*—of lack of adequate diet because of shortage of money, of hopeless housing arrangements, with a troop of children who are constantly a prey to every passing infection. A sympathetic young G.P. is filled with compassion and may spend much time enlisting help on this family's behalf. The M.S.W. will have met many of these households in her family casework training when she spends two precious months of summer vacation toiling round the dusty back streets of London or Liverpool, investigating applications for help. She may find on presenting the facts to a kindly but shrewd committee that there are gaps in her knowledge and that she has been well and truly taken for a ride. One develops an awareness in listening to sad tales! They come from families who need to be approached with skill and imagination if they are not to become even more dependent and demoralized. Inquiry will often reveal that they are already well known to many social agencies, the Ministry of Social Security, the Welfare Officer, the Childrens' Department, possibly also the 'Cruelty Man' or the Probation Officer and perhaps the Vicar. Staff in the Family Service Units, a Quaker movement, have pioneered methods of helping these families by befriending and working to get through to them by any means possible, scrubbing floors and washing clothes or other basic tasks which may be shared with a mother in an attempt to give her fresh heart. The work calls for patience and faith because progress is slow—one may have to wait a generation to see the results of one's labours. Little can be achieved by dabbling with such families—it is better to give emergency help in crisis and otherwise leave the field clear for those undertaking the work. Many statutory authorities have now followed the Quakers' lead and have assumed responsibility. Sometimes an officer in the Welfare Department or one of the H.V.s specialize in this work. It is important for all concerned with a handicapped family to be aware of others in the situation and to agree upon who should be responsible for maintaining the regular contact and carrying through the treatment plan, calling on colleagues when this is indicated. Although it seems hard to view in this way, these families can absorb a disproportionate amount of time and energy. Time spent for results achieved has to be measured; prevention of crises by attention to early signs of distress in more competent families may be of higher priority for M.S.W. and G.P.

Reviewing my work over these three years in the practice, I was concerned to see that a few households had had a much larger proportion of my time than the majority and that in some of these I could claim very little constructive result.

Example. Imagine a time when a patient was referred for social assessment. When admitted to hospital her condition ceased to be troublesome, but was as bad as ever immediately she returned home. The marriage of a favourite son seemed a factor. The patient resented a rival for the son's affection and his wage packet. The girl had been on probation and under supervisory care where she had performed well. Marriage had followed upon pregnancy and she had not settled to housekeeping duties—apparently their makeshift caravan home was too isolated. The mother-in-law's martyr attitude was tiresome and, while trying to be impartial, my enthusiasm to give the younger woman a chance to show her worth rather obscured my judgement! They came to me for help with the H.P. A voluntary loan was raised but they failed in payments and would never have honoured the agreement had not the H.P. manager seen fair play. The couple continued to have periodic splits and the boy has been in trouble at work.

Example. In contrast, another young couple were referred because the marriage seemed on the point of breaking up. The girl's parents who had come to 'help out' at the time of her second confinement, had always been critical of her husband who seemed to go out of his way to be boorish. He was in fact a good worker who had stuck to an apprenticeship, established his own business, and started buying their home with little help from his own family. The wife had also had her troubles with an unloving stepmother. For both partners therefore the marriage and family meant a great deal. Discussion of the husband's possible feelings and the early responsibilities of marriage—when the man is working hard to provide for the family and the wife's attention is so centred on the babies—led to better mutual understanding. Relations have been happier since then.

I had spent less than four hours on the second couple in contrast to nearly thirty hours on the first couple, where the results had been minimal.

Both G.P.s and social workers are swamped with calls upon their time and sympathy. It seems vital to consider in each case whether patients can make use of the help one is offering, whether they show real motivation, for instance, in keeping appointments or following up any plan agreed. These families are not primarily medical problems and I think a M.S.W. can help her G.P. colleagues in making such assessments.

Medical problems

A third group of patients where the M.S.W. has a contribution are those with physical illness or disablement. It is important to treat the disease but also to be aware of the personal implications.

Example. A middle-aged man had had a stroke. There was some incontinence but no severe paralysis and good medical care had got him to the point of being ambulant, though he was no longer fit for work. The couple had moved to this area fairly recently, and had undertaken a great deal of decorating themselves. One day, in an attempt to help his wife and to occupy himself, Mr. W. took a hand in stripping the wallpaper, but only succeeded in creating a fall of plaster. For his wife, tired out by waiting on a retarded shuffling husband, and having to assume the main burden of the home, this was the last straw—she took an overdose of tablets and had to be rushed to hospital. The patient here was frustrated by his own impaired function and bored by lack of activity. His wife had to come to terms with her husband's changed personality and the increased physical work which fell upon her. They were put in touch with the County Occupational Therapist who visits the disabled. After irritating delays, it was possible to obtain an incontinence appliance which eased the laundry problem for the wife and made it possible for the patient to mix with others at a workshop for disabled people and to attend social gatherings. A place was also booked for him at a seaside holiday camp for the disabled run by voluntary effort. His wife was able to have a complete break.

Cases of chronic disablement call for considerable adjustment on the part of near relatives and all possible help should be given. If the patient can be helped to occupy himself some of the satisfaction of former achievement and activity may be regained.

Cheerful and understanding social contacts can help both patient and relatives to take fresh heart and not to feel isolated and overwhelmed by the disablement.

Practical services such as domestic help or nursing equipment should be easily and quickly available and finance should not be a bar. A M.S.W. should know about procedure for claiming statutory allowances and the many voluntary funds which provide for different groups of patients.

A periodic break from caring for the patient can mean the difference between a nervy overwrought relative, hardly able to conceal resentment, and one whose normal affectionate attitude to the patient is unimpaired. I think this help is essential to anyone carrying the responsibility of constant care.

To summarize, three categories of patients may commonly need medicosocial help:

1. Patients who repeatedly come to the G.P. with symptoms, but without demonstrable disease; and those patients who remain unwell after a physical illness.

2. Social inadequate patients.

3. Families with a continuing burden of chronic disablement.

3. The doctor-patient relationship

General Practitioner and patient reactions to the Medical Social Worker

I have suggested different groups of patients where an M.S.W. may have a contribution, but what about the patients' views on being handed on? Will they feel fobbed off if their G.P. does not share their problems himself? Will this lead to impersonal medicine? They have presented at surgery with what they regard as a medical problem—will they be affronted if it is suggested that they are in need of social help? The patients here have seldom found any difficulty in accepting this relationship and I think this is because they have connected me so closely with the practice. They know that their G.P.s are not ceasing to care for them, but rather wanting to provide every possible form of help.

The second point is that, when referring a patient to his own social worker, the G.P. is not withdrawing from the situation. The M.S.W. should be keeping him up to date with her findings and he is often seeing the patients or relatives on medical matters.

Example. A housewife was referred with a history of post-puerperal depression and anorexia. She had several teenage children by a previous marriage which had failed. Her present husband was apparently much more considerate, sharing the housework and showing his concern by consulting the G.P. about his wife's state. She was always polite but unforthcoming and did not make it easy for the rushed G.P. to size up the situation. I could spend more time and she eventually revealed marital difficulties. She had seen this second marriage as a business arrangement, the husband would have a home with her and the family in return for his financial contribution—not surprisingly, this was not entirely the answer for him. His lack of confidence in her affection showed itself in jealousy of the children and closeness with money, both of which hurt and puzzled her. We considered whether it might help her husband to discuss the situation and agreed that he might find it easier to put his point of view to another man. The G.P. had been kept informed and when the husband appeared in surgery was able to help him talk without embarrassment. He and his wife have since come to a happier understanding together and there is a different atmosphere in the home.

Two points about this case are significant: the way in which G.P. and social worker shared the 'casework' role, and the fact that following the social referral, the patient then talked more freely with the G.P., revealing to him some material which she had not mentioned to the social worker. Dr. Huygen in Nijmegen found that his patients regarded his employment of a social worker as a sign that he took account of the human aspect of illness. Having been encouraged to talk about this aspect with the social worker, they talked more freely with him.

The busy G.P.'s reaction may be that his problem is not to get his patients to talk but to limit the length of their consultation. The contact with the M.S.W. may help here. One of the objects of casework is to help a patient to get his problem clear in his mind; this helps to limit it and it becomes less overwhelming. In talking with the M.S.W. the patient should have been helped to sort out the situation so that the main elements stand out clearly and the steps needed to reach a solution may be defined. Subsequent discussions with the G.P. should be calmer and more purposeful.

It is not easy to find objective criteria for measuring the effect of a M.S.W. in a situation. The medical consultation rate has been suggested as a guide, but patients may have to attend for reasons unrelated to personal situations, for instance, for routine ante-natal care or control of chronic conditions such as pernicious anaemia. A G.P. in another practice with M.S.W. contact has defined it more in terms of a change in patients' behaviour—he finds that where the M.S.W. has been introduced there is a reduction in tension, those patients are less pressing and unreasonable in their demands on him and they are calmer in subsequent discussions of the problem. G.P.s in Nijmegen and here in England have also made the point that, even in situations which are irreversible, it is a help to have a full social assessment. Future goals in management of the case can then be set more realistically.

4. The Medical Social Worker's possible contribution to medical education

It may seem presumptuous to suggest that social workers have a contribution to make in helping doctors to develop social awareness, but I think it is true. Medical advances in the past fifty years have transformed and even given life to many patients—diabetics or patients with pernicious anaemia now not only survive but can enjoy life. Patients no longer succumb *en masse* to infectious diseases in this country. There have also been advances in understanding the human mind and feelings, but until recently this has not been so widely recognized or accepted by the medical profession as a whole. The vagaries of human emotions cannot be measured or predicted in quite the same way as a patient's weight or blood pressure—though they may well have a bearing on both. One also hesitates to probe lightly into another human being's feelings and relationships. But where there are obvious signs of unhappiness and dysfunction, sometimes expressed in physical symptoms, surely one is moved to try to help and cure, as one is in the face of physical illness.

I have been proud to work with many doctors who were skilled and gentle in their care of patients but I have known others, equally sincere in their concern, but unable to make contact or to put their medical explanations into words the patient could understand. Patients often make the doctor's task more difficult by investing his every phrase with the import of Holy Writ. This can mean great strain however, if he has said to an already hard-pressed relative that a demanding old lady should *never* be left in future, and this is interpreted literally. I think doctors need help in developing their awareness of their audience. One should be discriminating in choosing words to discuss the patient's management with, say, an educated relative and an immigrant worker—and one should also be sensitive to how much the listener has understood and interpreted one's advice! One's own grasp of a tricky personal situation may be ahead of the patient, but one needs skill in guiding him to this point of awareness if one's explanation is not to arouse hostility or complete denial. Timing is all important.

I know from work with medical students that guidance on how to communicate with patients is gladly received and fully used. On one occasion at Edinburgh the subject of the dying patient was discussed. One of the doctors spoke of his Army service and his conviction that wounded men faced death with great bravery as long as the M.O. and his staff stood by them and gave them support and companionship in taking the last lonely step in life. There are many who find a way of giving comfort and support in face of serious illness but it is not easy and there is a temptation to deny it, to avoid the patient or to be out when the relatives are calling. One may consider that such teaching is only relevant for social-work students —for those directly concerned with welfare. In the social medicine programme at Nijmegen, there is also a team approach, specialists from the social sciences—psychology, sociology, medicosocial work—joining medical colleagues in teaching seminars. The students are responsible for their own cases and consider such problems as the handicap of deafness or mental dullness in relation to the patient and family. The student himself finds out about social provision for the education and employment of such patients and considers the possible effect on family and community relationships. This knowledge is not just an interesting social aside—it will be directly relevant for any doctor treating the family and especially for the one responsible for their general medical care. Doctors have many different gifts and some may have more skill in surgery or research than therapeutic listening but all whose work is concerned with people have the responsibility of seeing that this side is provided for, perhaps by delegation to M.S.W. colleagues.

Every M.S.W. has to learn how to approach difficult situations with her patient, how to enable them to unburden themselves and share fears and troubles, not to block them when they need the relief of weeping. This skill can be taught and anyone entering a profession such as medicine or the Church could be helped by such teaching instead of being left to flounder, to learn the hard way, or perhaps to contract out and fail his patient. This does not mean necessarily probing into sensitive areas or forcing patients to put their feelings into words, but giving them a sense of one's understanding and readiness to help if they want to use us in this way. Sometimes feelings are too intense to be put into words until after the worst period is over.

Example. I was working with a widow some time ago who had nursed her husband during a long illness. They had known each other from childhood and it had been a happy marriage, as they both enjoyed the social activity of their hotel work. It took some time to help her find an acceptable substitute—interest, and tactful support was needed—she was accustomed to presenting a poised cheerful face to the world and this was a difficult period. It was suggested she might take student boarders and this has proved a great success—she would make a delightful understanding landlady and the contact with young life is helping her. She rang to tell me of her meeting with the pleasant students and their parents and it was at this point that she really put into words her feelings of loss and confusion following her husband's death.

5. A definition of casework

There is a mystique surrounding the term casework—as if it were something high-powered and esoteric; or a jargon term used by dabblers in amateur psychology. Casework is a working method of helping people with social difficulties. It offers the client two elements:

1. A trained understanding of human problems and reactions;
2. A respect for him and his ability to work out his own salvation.

A trained understanding of human problems

How far is a M.S.W. aiming to be a psychiatrist? We are not trained to treat psychotic patients, those with a mental illness where their sense of reality is seriously impaired. However, life is complex today and there are many people seeking support and help in contending with their problems. Many of these queue up in the G.P.'s surgery. Dr. Harrington, Consultant Psychiatrist in Birmingham at an address given to G.P.s in 1957 (7), said:

The bulk of straightforward psychotherapy is already done in general practice, and this is likely to continue to the betterment of general practice and psychiatry. Not every neurotic or 'functional' disorder needs specialist attention. Many patients are frightened by being sent to a psychiatrist, and some refuse clinic appointments for this reason. Hence the general practitioner has to practise psychotherapy in one form or another, whether he likes it or not. The problem is to make this form of treatment more effective and widely applied. . .
In point of fact, much effective psychotherapy is done without recourse to the unconscious mind and without speculations about repressed conflicts and motivations. Indeed too much sophistication in mental mechanisms, and too little common sense may be a positive hindrance to success.
What is Psychotherapy?

Broadly speaking any form of treatment designed to produce a response by its mental rather than its physical effects is psychotherapy. Such treatment falls into two groups. The first (which has been aptly called bedside manner or prescribing the doctor) uses suggestion, persuasion, re-education, reassurance and support. It includes managing the patient's problems and bringing about changes in circumstances which are noxious to him. This kind of psychotherapy is most suited to general practice.

This was echoed more recently by Dr. John Horder in the memorial address mentioned earlier (17). In defining psychological medicine, he speaks of:

the largest group of problems which the G.P. must deal with and which can still be considered psychological medicine, the anxieties, the miseries and the psychological gains which accompany so many ordinary physical illnesses and injuries. So far this list has been entirely of the problems of individual patients. But many of the problems which must be included in psychological medicine are problems of relationships between two people. The most important couples are husband and wife or parent and child. Occasionally, there are related problems in every member of the family. There is one more sort of relationship problem which can be very important for the doctor—that is his own relationship with his patients.

Considering improved physical and psychological methods of treatment he says:

Some patients cannot be cured or even relieved of the symptoms they bring unless their deeper problems are gently exposed. The technique is by listening and giving time for this. Diagnosis is achieved by doctor and patient together trying to understand what the real problem is. This involves the doctor in psychotherapy. Within certain limits, psychotherapy is inevitably the G.P.'s task. He should learn to do it well, partly by becoming more aware of his own emotional reactions to patients.

These are also the caseworker's tools—listening, support, reassurance, interpretation. A caseworker's training does include lectures and demonstrations in psychology, and rightly so—the work of Freud on human personality and more recently such specialists in child development as Erikson and Winnicott have contributed much to understanding the root causes of disturbance.

One is also offering a trained understanding of behaviour and ways of meeting stress. A M.S.W.'s training is designed to increase her awareness of the human aspects of illness and how difficulties may be overcome. Her whole purpose is to help her patient come to terms with his disability so that life may be full and satisfying for him. In a case of heart disease the doctor's training equips him to assess the physical factors, the blood pressure, the exercise tolerance, the clotting time. The M.S.W. will be wondering about the patient's attitude to his condition, whether he is over-cautious, exerting himself too much, frightened, anxious about his family. It is her job to know about his home conditions, his trade, the hobbies he enjoys. Both will be aware of the importance of physical and social factors, but one will be more highly trained to treat the physical, the other the social.

To understand the special problems of how sick and disabled people react, the M.S.W. has to consider human relationships in general—the way a child develops, his position in the family, his feelings about his parents, about other children who claim a share of their affections. One has considered the problems of adolescence, questions of employment and industrial relations. Troubled unhappy people do not always find it easy to express their hurt feelings. They may sit tongue-tied yet pleading for one's understanding, or covering up with a flow of chatter about the weather or any topic except the one which is worrying or upsetting them. The caseworker must learn when to speak, when to encourage with a question, and when to give the patient time to screw himself up to confide.

When I came to the practice, the partners asked for a description of a M.S.W.'s work—after listening to such a description, one of the partners commented that he found it interesting because this is what a G.P. is doing all the time, but I had put it into words. Where the G.P. is working by intuition, the caseworker's awareness of these reactions has been refined by training. She should be able to interpret the patient's behaviour and history and to make a clear social assessment, to 'put it into words'. She may spend some time talking with the patient and may see him on several occasions but her interviews are not just friendly chats, they have a purpose and direction, sometimes encouraging the patient to talk freely, sometimes bringing him back to a certain theme. They are aimed to help caseworker and patient gain an understanding of the problem and his feelings about it and how it may be tackled. The opportunity to talk out the situation to a sympathetic and understanding person may be sufficient to enable the patient to tackle his own problem. One is sometimes too close to one's own family to discuss problems without appearing to criticize, and outsiders may gossip. A patient has sometimes come with a problem such as family tension or job difficulties. I have gathered the facts and offered a further contact, perhaps a week later. While I am still speculating how to help, the session has helped him get the situation clear in his own mind. He has been able to open the subject with relative or employer and a better understanding has already been reached with the minimum of help. The patient has dealt with his own problem and this is the ideal solution.

Example. A mildly depressed housewife was referred because she needed a holiday from the care of her mother, a fine old lady of over 90 who is still knitting seaman's jerseys for her grandsons! We discussed various possibilities—enlisting the help of relations or friends or arranging a stay in convalescent home or geriatric hospital. The daughter then remembered a friend living nearby. If she would come this would be the solution. She wrote to tell me that this was fixed up and thanked me for all my help!

In a more difficult relationship situation, the caseworker may have to help without seeing the other parties concerned. One must be flexible in each case and one can still help through one's contact with the patient—gradually he comes to understand the situation and the other party's possible feelings more clearly, becomes more relaxed and there is more chance of reaching a better understanding.

Example. An attractive housewife had left her husband because he devoted all his time to his widowed mother and seemed unaware of the claims of his wife and baby daughter. She came to the surgery in distress, as her desperate move had produced no immediate effect and she was now contemplating legal action. Her G.P. was concerned that there should not be further estrangement and referred her instead to me. The young man was an only son and strong parental ties had been heightened when he had gone through a serious illness. The girl was absorbed in their charming baby daughter and had not alllowed for the fact that her husband's reactions might be not so intense, even though he was fond of the child. She herself was tolerant and generous enough to come halfway in considering her mother-in-law. She felt that her husband might be sensitive about her seeking my help and hesitated to mention surgery consultation. It seemed that my job here was a holding operation, supporting her while she remained away long enough to show her husband that he would have to make a choice between mother or wife, and doing what I could to help her understand her husband's position, so that when they met she could be as warm and tolerant as possible and there would be more chance of reconciliation. They are back again together and all is well.

I have tried to discount any suggestion that casework is a mysterious skill only to be practised by an *élite*, but I should like to be equally emphatic that practising without a sound knowledge of human behaviour is wrong and dangerous. This knowledge may not be gained in a quick or superficial way. It calls for study and supervised practice and involves the student in a greater awareness of her own personality and attitudes as these will influence her work with clients. This calls for breadth of character and maturity in the worker.

Respect for the client's ability to manage his own life

It may seem unnecessary to mention respect. Surely everyone respects the patient, but how often has the plan for an old lady's care broken down because the well-meaning planners did not risk discussion with the old person concerned, did not give her the time to turn it over in her mind, to put forward her wishes, to feel that she was still independent enough to have a say in her own destiny? For most healthy people it is not easy to have to rely on others—to be physically helpless and unable to dress oneself or run a house, to be handicapped and unable to do a man's job. People respond to such reverses in different ways—where one may react by hostility and aggression, another may become depressed, whilst a third may contract out by denying that there is any problem at all, for instance the hemiplegic, who refuses to acknowledge any difficulty in managing alone at home. Unless one understands the behaviour and the underlying cause, one may regard the patient as rude or ungrateful and fail to give help. Our society is complex and swift moving, and it is too easy to lose sight of the individual, 'to treat you as if you were just a number', as a disabled man said of his employers, a government organization, all too ready to off-load this less-productive cog in the machine.

Attitudes to social failure go back into the past. With the upheavals of the Industrial Revolution and later the Depression, there were extremes of poverty and wealth. There were eventually reforms but the unfortunate were not encouraged to seek help. Poverty was related to morality and relief was dispensed with stern injunctions as to proper conduct and humility. There were the 'deserving' and the 'undeserving' poor. It was shameful to need help, a sign of failure and degradation. Old associations take a long time to clear away—charity has been hated and the earnest do-gooder may be shunned because she is a reminder of her more patronising predecessor.

It is sometimes suggested too that the Welfare State encourages people to be selfish and spineless as it now provides too much. The modern caseworker should have a sense of history and an appreciation of those attitudes. The patient soon senses one's understanding and this is the secret of establishing contact. If help is offered with tact and sensitivity, the patient's self-respect will be strengthened and the social worker's support will encourage him to take fresh heart and tackle his own problems instead of becoming more helpless and dependent. If this spirit prevails there need be no fear that a team approach means the end of personal medicine.

Example. Imagine the case of a family who are nearly the despair of community staff because of the wife's disablement, the husband's lack of co-operation and the children's rebellion. District Nurses and Home Helps do yeoman work faithfully each week so that Mrs. A. need not leave her own home for a chronic hospital. This patient's helplessness makes her suspicious of relatives and neighbours in case they exploit her, and they have aggravated helping authorities by their lack of co-operation. They are, however, contending with a great deal—Mrs. A. used to enjoy shopping and looking after her own home. Her disablement now makes this impossible. It is no small matter for Mr. A. to face the implications of his wife's gross disablement—she is now incontinent. He is a labourer and works long hours for his limited wage. There had been differences in the marriage and he was described as inconsiderate of his wife and rude to any visitors. His co-operation was obtained by recognizing that plans should be made for his meals when his wife went into hospital. He agreed to her treatment and visited her regularly, agreed to the children going to relatives and got his own meals. The house is bare and squalid and I had offered to redecorate the sitting room with voluntary help as Mrs. A. is housebound. Mr. A. not only paid for the materials but he and his son shared our work each evening and he has since tackled the kitchen. The neighbours lazing in the summer dusk encouraged our activities with ribald comments, but they were moved to tidy the front garden as a gesture for Mrs. A.'s return. The families on this estate are not noted for generosity towards each other but there are signs of more mutual trust now.

Work with this family involves skill in casework. When one considers their difficulties it proved simple to win the co-operation of this family and others surrounding them, but why does it not happen more often.

Casework is common sense—casework is having the imagination to foresee what might go wrong in a plan for an old lady's discharge and preparing for it in advance—casework is feeling sufficiently involved to accept the work and carry the responsibility.

6. A link with Community Services

I mentioned the bewildering number of social workers who might be concerned over a single family, the importance of friendly and effective co-ordination. I think the M.S.W.'s value as a liaison officer in general practice is as important as her diagnostic contribution. She is a social specialist and she should have good understanding of the powers and functions of social-work colleagues. Social services grew up piecemeal as fresh needs were demonstrated and public compassion extended to assume responsibility for many groups in society which were in the past left to the Church. This is a historical accident, the need for rationalization is well recognized now, and the work of such bodies as the Seebohm Committee is directed towards this end.

Recognition of public responsibility for those in need is the mark of a civilized state but there are many complications in the practical administration of such services—it is difficult to legislate for individual needs in providing a service which will offer equal rights to all, and there is the danger of rigidity and insensitivity in interpretation of policy.

Example. I have been concerned with a man in his early forties disabled by disseminated sclerosis. He was provided with a mechanical car by the Ministry of Health and although this increased his mobility he was not permitted to take his wife and children. This meant that they could never enjoy a family jaunt without outside help. It is already difficult to counter this man's sense of failure as head of his family and this situation undermines it even more. The extra outlay on a car to replace the standard single-seater issue cannot, of course, be dismissed lightly. The patient's family rallied round and paid the cost of a small second-hand car. They could not help with the additional cost of tax and insurance but this was already covered on his Ministry car, and it seemed reasonable to ask if it might be transferred to the new car—it would involve the Treasury in no additional expense. He was by now too disabled to drive himself and, because his wife would have to be the chauffeur, the Ministry could not help. The Ministry car was removed! Statutory regulations should allow for more flexibility and humanity if they are to help in individual cases of disablement.

A large number of our patients are geriatric and sooner or later a problem arises about their future care; they may have had a stroke or fractured femur and now need more help with feeding, washing and keeping warm than can be given by relatives and a visiting Home Help.

The State has accepted responsibility for ambulant old people and for the provision of homes, but these can only cater for a limited number and there is always a long waiting-list. When an old person is in need of care, a plan which will offer help at some unspecified time is not the answer. What happens in the meantime? The hospital is pressing for the patient's discharge, the Welfare Department will not commit itself to any date of admission—the answer may well be that unkind pressure is brought to bear on relatives or neighbours, who may themselves be elderly or too committed to assume responsibility or they would have offered before. The result is anxiety, resentment, and quite often the plan breaks down—the patient gives up the struggle and neglects herself, or there is a further accident and this time chronic hospital care is needed. This is a very expensive way of meeting the problem but, more important, all concerned have suffered much distress of mind because help that really meets their need has not been forthcoming at the right moment. One might claim that the patient has not been sufficiently far-sighted in getting his name on a waiting-list in good time—but old people so often cannot contemplate giving up their own homes until events force the decision. One has to be ready with help at the moment when it is needed.

An alternative possibility, and one which many old people prefer to even the best-run institition is that of boarding in a private household. Sometimes a retired nurse or a housewife whose family has grown up takes one or two old folk and the care given can be good and kind. The strict statutory regulations regarding washing facilities and fire escape sometimes limit the amount of help such volunteers can afford to give. Of course, these safeguards are important, but warm-hearted sympathy towards old folk is equally important. There needs to be flexibility in the way regulations are implemented—if finance is the bar to an otherwise suitable application, could not the local authority offer loan facilities to bring premises up to the required standard? There are reservations on the grounds that land-ladies might be more interested in profit than in caring for old people. This risk must be recognized, but in child care the benefits of family rather than institution are recognized and the risks are countered by careful selection and supervision of foster homes. In any case, adequate payment for a good job done is a reasonable proposition—landladies are not salaried like county officials. In Devon, the welfare staff have high standards of training which should give them skill to select the right personnel to care for old people.

The point I want to make is not necessarily that boarding out is the best solution but that, in preoccupation with regulations, statutory officers sometimes seem untouched by the human individual and his problem. The whole machinery is too slow and cumbersome and one is tempted to bypass it in dealing with an urgent problem. In our study the high number of consultations with other workers will be noted. In order to get a service implemented and see that the request is carried through, one's approaches to community colleagues often equal one's contacts with the patient. This point was made by Joan Collins—when she followed up patients several months later she found that in a large number of cases the contact established with the department concerned had been allowed to lapse. Clients' own lack of drive is often a factor which must be acknowledged, but departmental lack of personal commitment to the patient is certainly another. The budget for health and welfare services is limited and it is important that the services set up really do meet the needs of those for whom they are provided. In selecting personnel for any public service, a genuine warmth and wish to help people is as important as theoretical knowledge.

The G.P. has always offered a personal service and perhaps it is no accident that patients still turn to him more readily, even though there may be a statutory department provided to meet their need. The answer is surely close co-ordination of G.P. and statutory ser-vices. Consultation is a two-way process. It is sometimes difficult enough within the surgery to focus a G.P.'s attention for discussion of a patient's problem. His impatience, though understandable under current pressures, could be interpreted as lack of co-operation and I think G.P.s must come half-way with community workers. Yet, with the best will in the world, it is not easy for a rushed G.P. to differentiate between all the different social agencies. Then there is the time wasted trying to get in contact, finding that the worker is not available, then that she has rung back when he is out. The social worker must be immediately accessible if the doctor is to use the service. If there is a practice social worker she may either give assistance herself or help in the link-up with outside specialists. My community colleagues seem to have welcomed a contact within the surgery to help them pick the right moment to approach the different partners.

It is easy to state the virtues of good communication but not so simple to suggest methods—who does one communicate with and how often? One could spend one's entire time attending meetings and oiling wheels but there would be no time for seeing patients. I should like to mention two instances of colleague co-operation in Barnstaple which I consider have helped mutual understanding and have effectively improved service to patients.

A year or two ago, staff in the Youth Employment Service were concerned at their poor success in placing disabled youngsters and decided to invite all responsible to meet quarterly to discuss the needs of these young people. The group has brought together personnel in government departments such as the Ministry of Labour, the Ministry of Social Security, county officials from School Medical Service, Mental Welfare and Welfare Departments, and has drawn in other interested workers such as myself from general practice. This group has been absorbed in consideration of the problems on hand—no member has been less humane in his concern for the patients than another, and we have all gained in understanding the size of the problems and the issues involved in finding solutions. At a recent meeting a representative of the County Medical Department mentioned a projected sheltered workshop to be established in co-operation with the Ministry of Labour. It was felt that the views of the G.P.s would be valuable as to patients who have a need for this service. Data were collected and sent to the County Medical Officer. This seemed to me an example of good co-operation and policy planning.

This link with G.P.s has been welcomed and used by other social agencies. When there was a recent allocation of old people's flats, the Housing Department invited the partners to give medical opinions to ensure the fairest allocation. Concise information was given with the knowledge and approval of the patients, the doctors giving the medical opinions, the social worker adding social facts and collating the material as follows:

Elderly couple—frail.
Mrs. A. is diabetic, has had several strokes and cannot walk unaided. Husband cares for her and the house with the help of a daughter living near. Present house too large and without modern conveniences. Accommodation would have to be near daughter.

Elderly widow—sever chronic bronchitis.
Present accommodation is upstairs converted flat which is so unsuitable she has had to be hospitalized for the past two winters with resulting public expense.

Unsatisfactory housing is often at the root of a problem. Where a local practice and housing department can work together the G.P.'s time may be saved from special pleading on hard cases and it makes for fairer social policy all round.

Unceasing patient demands on the G.P. with heavy surgeries and visiting lists, make it impossible for him to attend many social welfare meetings but he usually has a full knowledge of families under consideration and can contribute valuable opinions. In each of the instances quoted, his views were sought by the authorities concerned and it was possible for him to give his opinion in a convenient way. I think that a practice social worker can help to make this possible.

It is vital that different helping professions have an effective link where they are jointly involved in families with special problems.

Example. One of my patients is an unmarried mother. Her father has a chronic mental condition. He is often restless and agitated, especially at night, which means that the others cannot even get proper rest. She has remained at home to stand by her mother, going out to work to provide for herself and her daughter. The daughter is now 13 and the normal adjustments of adolescence are made more difficult by the fact that she is so large that endocrine unbalance was suspected, though tests proved negative. The strain at home, together with self-consciousness at her size, was causing the girl to withdraw into herself and the young mother was at a loss how to help. The girl attends the secondary school where there is good understanding of individual difficulties. It was invaluable to have their views on this girl's aptitudes and school behaviour, and additional information on the home circumstances enlarged their awareness of the girl's difficulties. She has marked artistic ability and will be guided as to career prospects in this field. The school have also made a uniform grant to assist with clothing, quite an important factor for an adolescent girl, and one which will ease the mother's financial difficulties.

Example. An hydrocephalic boy was referred. He had done well, but, as adolescence approached he was becoming more self-conscious. With a physical handicap and some degree of intellectual limitation, help would also be needed to place him in a secure job which would both interest him and be a realistic choice for his abilities. His home was a very helpful one and his teacher in the remedial class at the secondary school is an understanding and encouraging man. The boy's ambition was to be a G.P.O. telegraph boy and he had shown his energy and perseverance in joining with his school mates in a marathon seventy-mile cycle ride for a Duke of Edinburgh award—he arrived home at 2 a.m. but had completed the course! Discussions have taken place at home, school, and Ministry of Labour, and the boy will be considered for a vacancy when he reaches entry age at Easter, well before competition from the rush of school-leavers in July. When remedial teacher and Youth Employment Officer were both doing an excellent job, one may well ask how they might feel about a social worker taking up their time in discussion on individual children, when the overall provision seems so well thought out. Rather than regarding it as unnecessary interference, they have welcomed the link with the medical side, and recognized our mutual concern for the child under discussion.

If there could be more pooling of thought on a child's progress it might make it more possible for us to recognize and check trouble earlier where there is risk of disturbance or delinquency. Again, one is aware of the need to be alert to vulnerable situations.

Example. Take the case of another household where the mother is borderline mental defective and was early abandoned by the father. The eldest son was discharged by the Army because of epileptic signs never medically confirmed. He was immediately in trouble with the Courts. Barnardo's have taken him back into care to save the mother from further bullying. There is a second child, a bright and appealing girl in her early teens, but quite out of control, with little respect or sense of law. The Probation Officer is struggling to save her from corruption but her attitudes may well be too fixed now to save her from her own blindness. Discussion with school staff revealed that this child had been a source of concern for at least three years, for constant disobedience, unreliability, petty thieving. Perhaps if school staff, G.P., and Mental Welfare Officers had had a better link-up, effective help might have checked this train of events.

7. The Health Visitor

The G.P. needs a link with Community Services and it has often been suggested that the H.V. as one of the team of county staff, is the obvious choice to be the G.P.'s social worker. In talking with H.V.s and reading I have been struck by the similarity of patient range which is the concern of both M.S.W. and H.V. The H.V.'s nursing knowledge enables her to be a helpful assistant in medical follow-up, seeing that medication is understood and that the patient remains in balance. It can also be a great reassurance to young mothers to consult their H.V. where the G.P. may not be so readily accessible. The H.V.'s point of entry on some matter of practical procedure or information may be an easy lead-in if the patient is wanting help on more personal matters—when one is weighing the baby or discussing feeding difficulties it can be easy for the mother to confide any fears. Nurses and physiotherapists also find this. H.V.s help in health education at schools and in preparation for marriage classes—an individual who may not have courage to speak up in the open class may well approach the teacher afterwards and voice some difficulty. The trend towards group techniques is an interesting one, and much can be done to spread scarce professional skill to benefit the greater number—after-care for psychiatric patients may be developed in this way, or preventive work done before a young couple run into difficulties in early marriage. It may be that this is the most effective way of helping people with simpler troubles, but when she is approached on a personal problem it is important that the H.V. has an adequate appreciation of the material being produced, the implications in the emotional situation on which she is being asked to help or advise, and that the help given is expert and unhurried. This perception is not developed simply by attending refresher courses or reading a textbook. This is now appreciated by the H.V.s' training body and more training is being given in interviewing and the study of family problems.

Human relationships are complex—a problem may be solved simply by putting it into words, so clarifying the issue. On the other hand, patients' reactions may have roots in earlier relationships and experiences, the effect of which has to be clearly understood so that help may be sure and perceptive. Much patient work may be needed to help one client towards a fuller understanding of his own reactions and those of others connected with him. A caseworker also needs skill in assessing where a patient is incapable of modifying attitudes.

The time factor is a point which needs to be fully appreciated because it affects the number of patients a worker can cover. In many county departments, caseloads are so heavy that it is impossible to give a regular after care service—the contact cannot be more than superficial. Over the past year we have had H.V. attachment to the practice. Our two H.V.s are first rate. I think we have all enjoyed working together and the feeling that we could rely on the others having the same concern for patients. I would sometimes have liked to mention a need in a family with young children where I knew the H.V. would be involved, but have hesitated to put any additional burden on them, knowing they already had more than enough to do, and that the problem needed time if it was to be effectively tackled.

If a H.V. is expected to give a casework service, she needs more training and a smaller caseload. The fully trained caseworker is a specialist and her skills are most fully used on the most intractable social problems. Not every H.V. wants to work in this way. She eventually has to decide where her greatest interest lies, in using her highly developed nursing skills or in becoming a social worker.

I believe these points should also be appreciated by employing bodies aiming to provide a medical social service in the community.

8. Recording and reporting—for future study

In this experiment as with others elsewhere, we have found that a M.S.W. can be accepted and make a helpful contribution in general practice.

The M.S.W. is a specialist and when the G.P. refers patients he wants her to make worthwhile assessments, taking time if necessary, where he cannot spare it. Where I think that my work could have been streamlined was in administration and especially on recording methods. When a doctor comes into general practice, he has to change from hospital records with the traditional ordered history, to a bundle of large postcards condensing his notes on a consultation into one or two lines, yet not omitting any important point. M.S.W.s developed the practice of full narrative recording because the interview is one of our most important treatment methods. We may do all sorts of things to help a patient in practical ways, but it is as important to help him to think out his problems and come to terms with his feelings about it—this can only be done by listening and talking with the patient. Full records of interviews show the progress in the patient's thinking, whether he is able to modify his attitude or whether he repeats the same material at every discussion, unable to alter his position. Full recording also helps us to think back over the interview, to see points in their whole context, to note discrepancies we may have missed, leads we have still to follow up. This recording is valuable, but it is time-consuming to write and read, and I suggest that we need to be more discriminating in our use of it, and ready to try varying methods. When I came into general practice I was urged 'to send telegrams instead of letters', to devise some form of short-hand.

I should like to know how far tabular methods of summarizing information are suitable for our work.

We have for long been able to define certain areas of relevant data:
Composition of the household.
Work history.
Medical history.
However, our social records are not sufficiently flexible to record changes in the situation yet still give a clear picture. How many of out case fronts would be informative or even comprehensible handed straight to a doctor seeking basic data on the social situation?

I was interested to see the case sheet reproduced below used for homebound patients registered with some county authorities. This is designed to show information on a specialized group of patients but I was impressed by its clarity and conciseness.

For purposes of social inquiries, the Dutch have set out data relevant to social history in tabular form. They are rather daunting documents which read like foreign phrasebooks, in which every possible calamity

Fig. 14

........................County Council—Health Department
Welfare of the Physically Handicapped

Name........................Date of Birth.........M/S/W........
Address ....
Change of address...
Age at which disabled ....
Disability ....
Education (if under 16) ....
Training ....
Former Employment ....
Present Employment ....
General Practitioner...
Consultant ....
Case Ex-Service...
Reg. D.P.E. Act 1944 No. ....
Means..
Rent..................... Rates.................................
Other occupants of household ....
Type of Housing ....
Case Notes..
....
....

and traumatic experience is provided for. A section on Parental Family includes questions on:

Whether parents are still living.

Age of parents now/at death.

Cause of deaths.

Age of patient when each parent died/disappeared.

Health of parents.

Father's occupation.

Details of the marriage—if any separation.

Whether patient was reared by parents, if not, by whom.

How many years was one parent alone, whether there was a subsequent marriage.

Size of parental family and patient's place in it.

Size of household if patient was reared elsewhere, and his place amongst any other children.

Age of parents at patient's birth.

Age when patient left home.

Length of time in present community.

There are sections on:

Education,

Vocation,

Marriage,

Children,

Illnesses,

and some interesting *Subjective questions* beginning with one on the harmony in the home.

I do not suggest that social workers should take a social history in this way—or that medical students should be led to think that, if dealing with feelings and attitudes, one can plod inexorably through every section as with a medical history and expect to get much idea of a patient's true feelings. I do think that if we social workers make the effort involved in defining the factors which may be relevant in a patient's situation our recording is likely to be more concise and our communication with other colleages more to the point.

These three years have rushed past and it has not been a long time in which to establish contact with patients and colleagues in a cautious, closely knit community. There is still so much for a successor to do and I suggest that consideration of recording and communication methods would be interesting and worthwhile. A social summary should be available on the medical card and perhaps a running record to keep the doctor informed of social action taken. We need to do more work on methods of recording without betraying patients' confidence or adding to filing bulk. Unless the social worker can adapt her reporting to fit in with general practice tempo her G.P. colleagues will be working without information which could be available and the patients will not have the full benefit of co-ordinated treatment.

Summary

This experiment has been absorbing and challenging. I believe that there is a place for a M.S.W. in general practice. Her most helpful contribution seems to me her training in social assessment and her knowledge of the Social Services. With these she may help G.P.s and community colleagues to ensure that health may truly be 'a state of complete physical, metal, and social well-being and not merely the absence of disease or infirmity'.

9. Analysis of factual information from the medical social worker's records

Age, sex and married state

The proportion of women (295) to men (114) in the series approached 3 to 1. Fig. 15 shows the proportion compared with that of the practice as a whole.

Fig. 15

	Males	Females
409 cases of the series	27·9%	72·1%
Practice as a whole	45·1%	54·9%

Fig. 16 indicates that:

(a) *Women in the reproductive period of life* accounted for over one third of the series (ages 15—44, 146 cases, 35·9 per cent.). In the same age group the proportion of women to men rose to nearly 4 to 1. (146 women to 39 men). This is read as confirming the experience of others that need for medicosocial help is high in this group.

(b) *Patients over* 65 accounted for 27·9 per cent. of the series (114 cases). Patients over 65 in the practice as a whole represent 18·4 per cent.

(c) Well over half of those over 65 were *widows or widowers* (68 out of 114). Widows and widowers together made up over one-fifth of the total series (22·2 per cent.).

Fig. 16. *Age, sex, and married state*

Age groups		0–4	5–14	15–24	25–44	45–64	65–74	75+	Total
Married	M			3	18	23	5	4	53
	F		26		63	28	12	4	133
Single	M			9	6	4	3	3	25
	F			26	13	11	6	8	64
Widow/Widower									
	M					2	5	16	23
	F				4	17	18	29	68
Divorced	M				1				1
	F			1	2	3			6
Separated	M				2	1			3
	F			1	10	5		1	17
Child	M and F		16						16
Total		Nil	16	66	119	94	49	65	409

This underlines the need of the geriatric group and the difficulties associated with bereavement and solitary living in old age.

(*d*) In contrast only 16 *children* under 15 were referred (3·9 per cent. of the series).

Social class

Distribution of the 409 cases of the series by social class (Registrar General) was as follows:

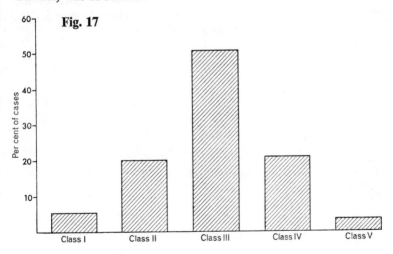

Fig. 17

It will be noted that the M.S.W.'s service has not been used only by those in the poorest social group. Money does not give immunity from old age or loneliness, or from other strains. This point was made by Joan Collins in her study in Cardiff, and our work would support it. Social services are so complex that all classes need guidance as to what facilities are available and procedures for obtaining them, for instance, supply of specialized equipment for the disabled.

Comparative number of cases referred to the Medical Social Worker by each General Practitioner

Owing to changes in the partnership and the presence of a trainee assistant in one year, several G.P.s took part in the experiment for a shorter period than three years. The annual referral rate of each G.P. corrected for this factor is shown below.

Although referral rates show variation between G.P.s, active participation by all members of the practice is indicated.

The variation in referral rates was partly accounted for by the method of communication—the three partners who had the highest referral rate all chose to have a regular session with the M.S.W. as distinct from an *ad hoc* arrangement. (They were not necessarily the partners who made the wisest referrals.) The M.S.W. did her best to give equal time to all patients but when a doctor is regularly watching progress it does keep her up to the mark! Para-medical workers can help most effectively if the G.P. reckons to devote some time and full attention to discussion of progress.

Fig. 18

General Practitioner	1	2	3	4	5	6	7	8	9
Time in experiment in years	3	3	2¾	2	3	3	2	¾	¾
Number of cases referred	25	57	35	57	107	74	40	5	9
Average Annual Referral Rate	8·3	19·0	14·0	28·5	33·7	24·7	20·0	6·7	12·0

Fig. 19. *Total time spent by the Medical Social Worker in hours per case.*

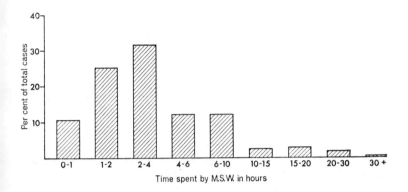

The time spent on cases by the Medical Social Worker

Fig. 19 below shows time spent on cases. The time recorded is an approximate measure of that spent on actual contacts with patients and workers. Travelling and administration is not included.

It can be seen that the time spent was 10 hours or less in 91·9 per cent. and 4 hours or less in 67·5 per cent. It should be noted that these figures and the figures below in Figs. 20–25 are *under-*estimates, as no allowance could be made for those cases where care was cut short by the ending of the experiment.

It can be seen that contact between the M.S.W. and patient was continued for more than 1 month in 86·6 per cent. and more than 4 months in 63·5 per cent.

Fig. 20. *Time-span of contact*

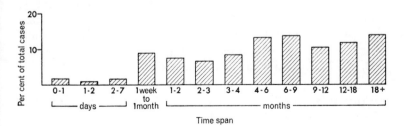

It is difficult to estimate the day-to-day caseload as it varies with the complexity of cases. The M.S.W. accepted as many cases as time permitted as she wanted to gather a representative number for the study. Looking back on this group of patients she tried to estimate the proportion of cases which could be closed after reasonable follow-up and the proportion where a continuing follow-up would be wiser. The results were as follows:

52·8 per cent. back in equilibrium;

47·2 per cent. likely to need continuing work as the risk of future breakdown is high.

For a large number of patients, help or information offered at a difficult time will be all that is needed to help the patient on his way. Should more difficulties arise in the future he will know what a casework service offers and the initiative can be left with him to return if in need. In an almost equally large number of cases, the problems were of such an irreversible nature that it seemed wiser for the social worker to keep the case open even though the contact might be infrequent. If one can manage a periodic follow-up, one is more likely to hear of changes or deterioration in the situation and help can be given in a planned way, rather than in emergency. I am thinking of cases where the patient was suffering from a permanent handicap, or a progressively disabling condition; or the sort of social situation typified by one of our families where the mother was absent, as she was in an epileptic colony. Here the father's skin reactions constantly threatened his earning ability—he was fond of his family and wanted to maintain responsibility for them. He had the doubtful help of the disabled grandfather who, until recently, was too independent to agree to any outside assistance, even that of a Home Help. This family will need support for some years to come.

This estimate is a purely personal opinion but it is based on field experience. It is important to be clear as to which patients can be helped by short-term treatment and which need a longer contact. On this will depend the number of cases a worker can carry and to which he can give an effective as distinct from a superficial service. The M.S.W. found the caseload with an average of 136 per year was heavy—100 would allow better patient cover. But it was felt that energy could have been saved on more efficient recording—this is discussed more fully on page 90.

Fig. 21

	Where patients' personality is an aetiological factor	Where interpretation is a form of the help given
Patients occupying the M.S.W. for less than 6 hours (326 cases)	42·9% of series	39·6% of series
Patients occupying the M.S.W. for more than 6 hours (83 cases)	78·3% of series	77·1% of series

We have compared the patients who were helped in a comparatively short time with those whose problems were less quickly treated (Fig. 21). Those whose problems demanded a relatively long time included a high percentage of patients with personality problems, and a high percentage for whom interpretation was a form of help given.

The number of home visits to patients and the number of surgery consultations

Visits include any working contact with the patient outside the surgery. Consultations include any contact inside the surgery, which may be face to face or a telephone link between patient and worker.

Only 12·7 were not visited at home. It can be seen that the majority (67·5 per cent.) were visited between one and five times. 9·1 per cent. were visited ten times or more.

Fig. 22. *Number of home visits*

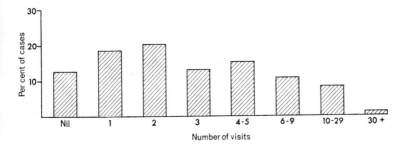

Fig. 23. *Number of surgery consultations*

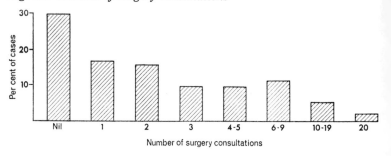

Number of surgery consultations

Nearly one-third of the cases (29·8 per cent.) had no surgery consultations; i.e. all consultation was carried out at home. Of the remainder the majority had from one to nine surgery consultations. The percentage of visits to consultations is partly affected by the office position. This is an old surgery and space is at a premium. As the M.S.W. had the use of an office at certain times only—it was sometimes easier simply to visit, although to see a patient in the office saved much travelling time in a scattered practice. When working with young families, a less interrupted interview with the mother was possible if the children were at home absorbed in their own play.

Elderly and disabled people cannot always travel easily. The home visit also gives an impression of the patient as he is on his own home ground. He is often calmer at home and in a better state to discuss his problem; and an impression of neighbourhood, and all-round relationship can be gained, which is invaluable.

Fig. 24. *The number of consultations between the Medical Social Worker and General Practitioner*

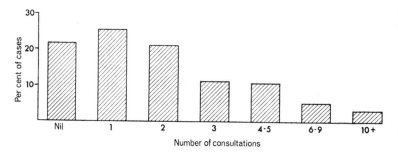

Number of consultations

Fig. 25. *The number of the Medical Social Worker's consultations with other colleagues*

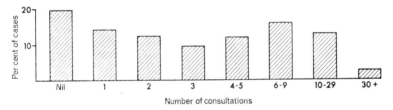

The referral consultation is not included nor the closing consultation. Consultation was most frequent where the M.S.W. needed guidance on a medical factor, or in joint plans to help a patient with a complicated problem.

This gives some indication of the time spent by the M.S.W. in case discussion with the members of the medical and social services and further illustration of her importance as a link between the G.P. and other services. The time required is one of the reasons why the work cannot be carried out by the G.P. himself.

The social agencies used by the medical social worker

The length of the list in Fig. 26 illustrates the large number of Social Agencies with which a G.P. is now expected to be familiar. The list is arranged in order of frequency of contact in this series. Frequency of contact may be some guide to incidence of need, but the absence of a good service also has a bearing. In this area this applies to the Psychiatric and Speech Therapy services. The Psychiatric cover, for instance, was provided from the nearest large centre, forty miles distant. Doctors at the fortnightly clinics often changed and were invariably rushed and preoccupied; and a different set of personnel cared for the patients in hospital. This important contact was therefore less available than one could wish from the point of view of patients and relatives. The Mental Welfare Officers were a helpful liaison but for a great deal of their time they were out of range as they were on the road, escorting admissions. In contrast the Welfare Officer for the Blind had been in the post for many years; she really knew her blind patients and was extremely well informed on services for them. If a patient was referred to her he was not left unvisited or unhelped.

The term kindly souls seemed the best one to describe goodhearted neighbourly people, sometimes without formal qualifications, who have been prepared to sit with patients, to relieve relatives at night, or to give invaluable help in emergency, without being trammelled by statutory regulations. Statutory provision for such needs is still inadequate—private fees for night attendance can be crippling and the strain of constant nursing can be exhausting.

The fund of goodwill in our society is considerable—among young people—among married women with time to spare—among church-going people. The pool of professional personnel is not likely to increase much, and one way in which we may spread our skill as far as possible is by working with such volunteers. They need our guidance and encouragement, and we need their time and good-heartedness. This can work as long as the social worker does not

Fig. 26. *List of the Social Agencies[1] used by the Medical Social Worker with the percentage of cases in the series involved in each*

Nil	16·4	Church	3·7
M.S.W. (Hospital)	12·5	Psychiatric Consultant	3·7
Employer	11·7	Appliance Officer	3·4
Welfare Department	11·5	Ambulance	3·4
Housing Department	10·3	Occupational Centre (Workshop)	3·2
Health Visitor	10·0	Consultants other than Psychiatrists	2·9
Voluntary Old Peoples' Homes	9·8	Police	2·4
Schools	9·8	Voluntary Convalescent Homes	2·2
Ministry of Labour	9·3	Other G.P.s	2·0
Kindly Souls	9·0	Education Department	2·0
National Assistance Board	7·8	Physiotherapist	1·7
Hospitals	7·3	British Red Cross Society	1·7
Mental Welfare Officer	6·6	Child Guidance Clinic	1·5
Women's Organizations	6·4	Speech Therapist	1·0
Home Help	6·4	Voluntary Nursing Help	0·7
Solicitor	5·6	N.S.P.C.C.	0·7
Occupational Therapy	5·4	Forces	0·7
Moral Welfare Worker	5·4	Men's Organizations	0·7
Ministry of National Insurance	4·4	Local Authority Development Clinics	0·5
Landlord	4·4	St. John's Ambulance	0·2
Voluntary Funds	4·2	Marriage Guidance Council	0·2
District Nurse/Midwife	3·9	Dentist	—
Children's Department	3·9	Play Groups	—
Probation Department	3·9	Others	16·6

1. We have used this term broadly—it includes not only statutory Social Services but all with whom the M.S.W. had a working contact in connection with the patient's social difficulties.

simply hand over and withdraw from the situation. She is still responsible and should be at hand to see that all goes well, that the volunteer's enthusiasm does not flag, and that the patient does not make unreasonable demands.

In 83·6 per cent. of the series one or more social agency was brought into play by the M.S.W. This underlines her contribution as a link between the G.P.s and the Social Services, and is in accord with the G.P.s rating of the M.S.W.'s contribution in Fig. 7. (Chapter 4) where 'Link with the Social Services' is given the highest rating in the types of service given.

PART THREE

Comments by General Practitioners
and Health Visitors

Comments by General Practitioners and Health Visitors

From **K. G. W. Saunders,** O.B.E., M.B., B.S., F.R.C.S.Ed.

The introduction of a M.S.W. into general practice is a recent idea and it is necessary to gauge how great a contribution she can make and in what direction and type of case she can be most effectively used.

It may be a help in deciding this to look back and consider how general practice has changed since, for instance, I started work forty years ago. Then the doctor not only treated patients who were ill—often desperately ill—but also was frequently asked to solve domestic and social problems or act as a contact with authority that the patient was not able to do personally. The former part of his work was often little more than a bolstering up of morale and helping nature to effect a cure; the latter might be quite an important contribution to the happiness of the family.

Comparing this with the present day we see that the medical demands on the doctor's skill in investigation, diagnosis, and treatment take up far more of his time, and the social problems which are now quite as insistent, often more so, cannot be given the attention they need. This is the sphere in which the M.S.W. can not only relieve the G.P. but can give even more effective help through her special training and availability of time.

The other great change that has affected the practice of medicine in the past twenty years is the extensive growth of the Social Services. But these services cannot be best applied unless they are linked up with the needs of the patient. Here the M.S.W. can be of great use, knowing the problem of the patient and having the knowledge of the particular service that can be of most help.

As I see it the G.P. in the future will need to spend more and more of his available time working on the increasing demands of medical diagnosis and treatment that only he can meet, while the M.S.W. can work with him in sorting out the social and domestic problems which are always present to a lesser or often greater extent in any illness.

In order to do this they should work as a team so that the whole picture is under review all the time from the original briefing by the doctor of the M.S.W., through talks on progress to an eventual satisfactory conclusion. This does mean some time spent in going into background, temperamental and other factors, keeping a watch on progress and exchanging ideas on various points and aspects of the case as they crop up. The time spent is, however, well worth while.

I have found that in working along these lines during this three-year experiment, there is undoubtedly a definite place for the M.S.W. in the social work of general practice. She can be of great help to the doctor and will find increasing opportunity in the future of enlarging her scope in this field. It has been my experience also that the patients themselves appreciate that there is someone else who is trying to help them and it gives them a further feeling of security. None in my experience have felt any sense of intrusion into their private affairs.

From S. G. Brook, M.B., B.Chir. (Cantab.), M.R.C.G.P., D.Obst.R.C.O.G.

The three-year study of the attachment of a M.S.W. to the group practice, now recently completed, was most interesting and instructive for those taking part. There were many problems to be solved, and much to be learnt. Two important changes took place during the three-year period. There were several unexpected changes in the members of the partnership, and two H.V.s were attached to the group practice by the Local Health Authority.

At first the partners had very little idea of how a M.S.W. set about her job, and how best to make use of her special training and experience. At the same time, the M.S.W. found general practice very different from the environment of hospital and training school, to which she was previously accustomed. After a while we learnt what should and what should not be expected of the M.S.W., and we also learnt that much more could be achieved by the surgery staff and H.V.s than hitherto, some of their previous working methods being more traditional than useful. This will prove a lasting benefit to the organization of this practice.

I think we could have achieved more, and learnt more, if we had been able to meet together more frequently. Our group meetings and discussions were helpful and stimulating, but it was very difficult to add such to a busy timetable, when we had not yet learnt what time we saved by having the help of the M.S.W.

Our attention was, not unnaturally, directed to social problems and Social Services. One important thing learnt was that there are large gaps in the public Social Services and at the same time many places of overlapping responsibility. To remedy these defects means more than co-ordination at a local level, a number of different ministries being involved. It is time for a major reorganization on a national level, thus saving much expenditure of money, and making better use of precious trained personnel.

Just as it is difficult initially to integrate a M.S.W. into a group practice, so it is difficult suddenly to lose her, and it is this sense of loss which brings home to one the great value of having such help in general practice. At the same time, the help given by the H.V.s has increased and expanded in its nature, and I, for one, am convinced that a reorganization of the training and experience of the H.V. would be a great benefit to the community.

A research project of this nature emphasizes the difficulty of such work while engaged in general practice. It takes much time and money but it is of great educational value to the participants, and may be helpful to all those interested in such work.

From **J. A. Smart**, M.B.E., M.B., B.S. (Lond.), D.A.

I was a member of the partnership for two out of the three years of this experiment, up to the time that I gave up general practice in favour of my hospital work. During this time, I had in addition to my general practice commitment, seven sessions in my speciality to do at the hospitals. This double commitment meant that I could do less in the general practice than many of my partners, but also meant that I was extremely glad of the help which the M.S.W. could provide in taking work off my shoulders where her specialized knowledge could be of value.

The type of case which I referred could be divided into three categories, thus:

1. Where I did not have the time to devote myself sufficiently to the domestic troubles of patients, which were having a definite effect on their general health or that of their family, but where I could have done the same as the M.S.W. if I had had the time to do so. Here the requirement was to listen to many tales of woe which where not directly related to the illness in hand and to offer advice over many minor problems which the patients were inadequate to deal with. These problems were very time-consuming for either myself or the M.S.W. but my impression is that after having been a major support for these patients over a period the M.S.W. has managed to get them much more socially adjusted and able to cope with their own problems so that when she ceases work the previous problem of constant calls on the doctor's time will be permanently diminished.

2. Where the M.S.W. could do what I could not, even given the time and inclination. The doctor sometimes cannot get beyond a certain stage with a patient who may often come from one of the lower grades of the social structure. Here, with the best will in the world on the part of the physician, there is a certain level of communication which the patient will give to an employee of the partnership or ancillary staff but which he or she will not give to the doctor himself.

This helpful insight can often be made use of by the M.S.W. where any other employee or ancillary would not be able to utilize it. I may be over-simplifying when I refer to information which can be transferred, as it is more a matter of *rapprochement* between patient and M.S.W., which is different (and potentially helpful) from that which exists between patient and doctor.

3. The side of the M.S.W.'s work which involves knowledge of parallel services available to the patient from the state or other sources:—National Insurance, Public Assistance, Charitable Trusts, aids for the physically or mentally handicapped, etc. Here the knowledge of what is available is of great assistance, and, in addition, the

time and trouble spent by the M.S.W. in contacting and dealing with these problems results in a tremendous saving of the doctor's time and patience.

From J. P. Bush, M.B., B.S. (Lond.), M.R.C.G.P., D.Obst.R.C.O.G.

There is perhaps in the mind of any G.P. who enjoys a family doctor type of relationship with his patients the idea that he is anxious, and indeed able to cope himself with all the patients' social, medicosocial, and family problems. However, in this age of specialization, he has no feeling of failure in referring patients in need of specialist medical and surgical care to the appropriate highly trained specialist, and as the association between medical conditions and diseases and their frequent origins in disturbed social relationships is recognized further, it is natural that the development in practice towards referral of social problems to specially trained medical ancillaries should be further recognized and accepted. The older G.P. has a wealth of experience in the broad field of medicine and great experience of life in general. However, few G.P.s have more than a very limited amount of experience, training, or knowledge of all the various Social Services available to help their patients with their varied problems.

Having had the good fortune to marry an Almoner (or M.S.W.), it was understandable that in my early years of practice I was ready to acknowledge and in fact look forward to the assistance such a trained person could give me in my practice. Therefore I welcomed the opportunity when it came through the initiative of Dr. Forman and the M.S.W. attachment project.

The first basic problem as I saw it was to decide whether the M.S.W.'s work within the practice should be as:

(a) trained ancillary help in the assistance with the organization and mobilization of other social services, or

(b) a 'para-medical worker' undertaking her own investigations of the problems of patients referred to her, for example, enuresis, asthma, etc.

In fact, experience taught that the M.S.W.'s work was a mixture of these two factors. The limitation of time prevented a full exploitation of all the possibilities of this second line of work, but, as the development of the H.V. system proceeded, a great deal of the former type of work (association with the other Social Services) was carried out by other persons.

I have no doubt that the value of a trained M.S.W. in a general practice cannot be assessed in any terms of time expended in briefing her. For the maximum benefit to be achieved from such an attachment I believe it is important that she be freed from routine procedures such as arranging for the provision of equipment such as wheel-chairs, hearing aids, etc. which should be undertaken by less skilled personnel. Her function should be to assist and advise both the patient and doctor in the many complicated medicosocial problems, and to undertake research in field-work in such subjects as asthma, enuresis, etc. for which the average G.P. has no time.

From a general practice in Australia, a land of comparatively high standards of living, with a private system of medical practice, and far less Social Services than in the U.K., I can only add my sincere thanks to Miss Fairbairn for all her help to me personally and my sorrow that I have not as yet any similar help in my own practice here!

From **D. B. R. Osborne,** M.B., B.Chir.(Cantab.), M.R.C.G.P., D.Obst.R.C.O.G.

My own reactions to working with a M.S.W. were at first defensive. I felt there may be loss of doctor–patient relationship, and this was just another agency added to all the other unco-ordinated Social Services available.

There has certainly been no loss of doctor–patient relationship and to be able to view the difficult emotional relationships found in a family involved in a long-term illness through two pairs of eyes, instead of one, has been invaluable, as inevitably there were often two view-points and interpretations of these situations.

Far from adding to agencies, it has been the correlation and pruning of the number of people involved with a patient which has been of particular value. It could not have been done by anyone other than a M.S.W. working from the practice.

It is almost impossible to assess the effect and result of introducing a M.S.W. to a situation, except that in the few months the M.S.W. has been away from the practice, a number of complex situations have arisen which, for lack of time and intimate knowledge of the available Social Services, I have not been able to deal with as effectively as a M.S.W.

In attempting to use a H.V. in situations where a M.S.W. would normally work, the most noticeable feature is the freedom of action available to the M.S.W. as opposed to the obligation to authority imposed on H.V.s which reduces considerably their effectiveness and limits their responsibilities.

Initially, communication was a problem, but after a while when the M.S.W. and myself had the measure of each other, less had to be said about the situations we were involved in.

Although the number of patients that no one other than a M.S.W. could deal with were small, the particular situations nearly always involved families who were suffering from chronic illness, physical disability, or mental illness, all of which involve the doctor in continuous care over many years. Here the M.S.W. should be able to take part in and share in the work on a long-term basis.

From **J. J. D. Bartlett,** M.B., B.S. (Lond.), D.Obst.R.C.O.G.

As a newcomer to general practice, I joined in this attachment during the second and third years. However, I found it particularly valuable in helping to sort out the social problems of the more minor, as well as a major, nature.

As regards the minor problems, I would indicate housing difficulties, pensions and insurance benefits, and arrangement of domiciliary ancillary help. These are small problems, but they can take up quite a lot of time, especially if you are unfamiliar with the details.

The more major problems, such as difficulty in adjustment to work, home, and children, as well as the all-important problem family, appears to me to be very much casework that cannot really be undertaken by the G.P. with his present time-schedule. These particular major problems are continually being bypassed or, more commonly, just handed from one department to another, so that they eventually come back to the G.P., who is asked to try and sort the mess out as best he can. The most important work to me of a M.S.W. is to take on these particularly difficult problems, to be able to spend the time in sorting them out and getting the right people co-ordinated, as well as keeping the G.P. fully informed. If this work is not done by a M.S.W. attached to a general practice, it will probably not be done at all under the present circumstances.

From **J.M. Lewis,** M.B., B.S.(Lond.), D.A., D.Obst.R.C.O.G

As a new extrant into general practice my medical horizons were, I feel, limited to clinical diagnosis and chemotherapy. I was from inexperience and training totally unprepared for the complexity of many of the cases which were to present themselves with minor organic symptoms.

After twelve months in a group practice, which was fortunate enough to have a M.S.W. attached, I have witnessed the happy solution to many problems for which I had neither the insight nor the time to analyse.

The referral must obviously come from the family doctor, who with experience and an occasional inspiration, appreciates the pressures that bring a particular patient to his surgery, and further analysis will often only be obtained with careful survey of the patient and family in their own home and environment. This detailed scrutiny is not to my mind within the province of the family doctor, who can best serve with clinical advice, discussion with the M.S.W. and prophylaxis at a later date to prevent recurrence.

There is no question of replacing the doctor by a M.S.W., but taken as an expert in her own field and incorporated into the management of selected cases, I can see nothing but satisfaction and success for the patient, practitioner, and M.S.W.

From **Phyllis Harper,** O.N.C., S.R.N., C.M.B., H.V.C. Health Visitor

*Thoughts and views arising out of the first
two and a half years of group attachment*

In October 1964 my colleague and I started working with a well-organized group practice. The partners believe in leaving as much as possible to a well-trained ancillary team; thus allowing themselves more time for the purely medical part of their work. From the beginning we were made very welcome, and soon felt ourselves to be part of a very hard-working but happy team.

Method of working. There are six G.P.s, with whom we work on a system of individual attachment. Our numbers of children under 5 years is about equal; but as this is an outdated method of assessing our work, perhaps I should mention that our practice looks after 14,400 patients. Of these, about half are in the town and half in the rural area. Very quickly I found myself referring to 'our practice' instead of 'my area'—a change which has made no difference to my annual mileage.

In the surgery we have our own shelf with our message books, and a tray for consultants' letters, etc., for us to read, before the receptionist files them with the patients' notes.

At a fixed session each week we see our partners individually to discuss work, and at any other time whenever the need arises.

On Friday afternoons we have a Well Baby Clinic, with Sister doing all the immunizations and vaccinations. We are just starting to change this to a Development Clinic with appointments. On alternate Wednesdays by appointment we invite mothers to bring their babies for the Routine Hearing Test.

For easy reference, a register is kept of all babies born in the practice, including transfers in and out. This register is kept in Sister's room, as she enters all immunization details.

The register includes details of:

(*a*) Category in 'At risk' register.

(*b*) Premature.

(*c*) Adoption.

(*d*) Phenistix test.

(*e*) Hearing test.

(*f*) Immunization.

(*g*) Vaccination.

(*h*) Boosters.

(*i*) Handicapped.

For the past three years a full-time M.S.W. has been with the practice.

She very quickly collected a heavy caseload of intensive casework problems, and proved the need for a trained caseworker in general practice.

It may be pertinent to mention here, that some people have asked if a H.V. could do the work of a M.S.W. in general practice. Even with my brief experience I feel the answer is 'No', not without a little more training, particularly in the skilful art of interviewing, and the interpretation of the information received.

One other important factor is that the M.S.W. is completely employed within her group practice—she has no other responsibilities towards any other authority. The H.V. on the other hand is employed by her Local Authority and has other duties outside her group practice—including adequate record keeping.

Although the pressure of work has increased on all sides, I feel that my short time in the practice has already broadened my outlook and enriched the purpose of my work.

From **Joan Dixon,** N.N.E.B., S.R.N., C.M.B., H.V.C. Health Visitor

My colleague and I were appointed as H.V.s to a G.P. group practice in October 1964. We were attached to individual doctors in the practice, enabling us to work as team members and to cover the area concerned, wherever our doctors had patients. This was a great step forward in getting away from the usual H.V.'s geographical area. The team of G.P.s, M.S.W., H.V.s, and ancillary staff has worked well for our patients and they, I feel, appreciate a personal service.

The co-operation between the M.S.W. and H.V. from the beginning of attachment has been good.

In my previous experience, the M.S.W. worked entirely from the hospital and I could not visualize her role in general practice.

Initially, there was the inevitable duplication of visits, but as we grew to understand and respect each other's special training this was remedied. In the main the social problems referred to Miss Fairbairn have been longer and more detailed, requiring the special skills of a trained caseworker.

Colleagues often ask the reason for both a M.S.W. and a H.V. in a group practice. Many feel that the H.V. training is sufficient. Personally I feel there is the necessity for both in a general practice. H.V.s carrying as they do the large case-loads and the fixed appointments at clinics and school have less time to deal with long complicated social problems.

The practice M.S.W. only dealt with G.P. referrals. She was completely independent and had no fixed appointments.

The surgery H.V. is employed by the County Medical Officer and seconded to the G.P. practice and must divide her time. All visits must be carefully selected, as many social problems are urgent, but at the same time general health visiting must be continued and fixed appointments kept. It is therefore impossible for a H.V. to cope alone with the medical social problems evident in group practice. The M.S.W. is invaluable to the team.

References

1. BACKETT, E. M., MAYBIN, R. P., and DUDGEON, YVONNE (1957.) 'Medico-social Work in General Practice', *Lancet*, 5 January 1957.
2. BALINT, MICHAEL (1964). *The Doctor, the Patient and his Illness* (Pitman Medical Press).
3. COLLINS, JOAN (1965). *Social Casework in a General Medical Practice* (Pitman Medical Press).
4. CROMBIE, D. C. (1963). 'Diagnostic Processes', *J. Coll. Gen. Practitioners*, 1. 107.
5. DONGRAY, MADGE (1962). 'Co-operation in General Practice', *Almoner*, vol. iv, no. 12.
6. —— (1958). 'Social Work in General Practice', *B.M.J.*, 15 November 1958.
7. HARRINGTON, J. A. (1957). 'Psychotherapy in General Practice', *Lancet*, 20 April 1957.
8. MERTENS, Professor ANTOON. Institute of Social Medicine, Nijmegen University, Holland (unpublished).
9. MORRELL, D. C. (1965). *The Art of General Practice* (E. & S. Livingstone Ltd.).
10. PATERSON, J. E. (1949). 'The Work of the Almoner in General Practice', *Almoner*, vol. i, no. 11. 232.
11. QUERIDO, A. (1959). 'Forecast and Follow-up', *Brit. J. Prev. and Soc. Med.*, vol. 13, no. 1 (1954).
12. SCOTT, Professor RICHARD (1949). 'The Almoner and the Family Doctor', *Almoner*, vol. i, no. 10. 209.
13. *Report of the Working Party on Social Workers in the Local Authority Health and Welfare Services* (Younghusband Report) (H.M.S.O., 1959).
14. *Reports from General Practice*. 1. 'Special Vocational Training for General Practice', (Coll. Gen. Practitioners, 1965).
15. *The Field of Work of the Family Doctor* (Gillie Report) (H.M.S.O., 1963).
16. WHITE, WILLIAMS, and GREENBERG (1961). *The Ecology of Medical Care*.
17. HORDER, J. P. (1966). *The Role of the General Practitioner in Psychological Medicine* (Albert Wander Lecture).
18. HUYGEN, F. J. A. Lent, Nijmegen.